BIOLOGY

Lab Manual

Science
Shepherd

SCIENCE SHEPHERD
BIOLOGY LAB MANUAL

Published by:
Ohana Life Press, LLC
1405 Capitol Dr.
Suite C-202
Pewaukee, WI 53072
www.ScienceShepherd.com

Written by Kathleen H. Julicher

ACKNOWLEDGEMENTS

Cover Design
Alex Hardin

Photo Credits
iStock.com

Graphic Illustration Credits
Sarah Constance Julicher, MD

Graphic Design
Jason Brown

ISBN: 978-0-9814587-1-7

Table of Contents

Materials List

LAB 2

Carrots or potatoes
Knife
Glasses (3)
Salt or sugar
Plastic wrap
Distilled water
Scale
Fruit
Bowl

LAB 3

Alcohol
Distilled water
Iodine
Methylene Blue
Microscope
Microscope slides: flat
Cover slips
Needle
Paper toweling
Round toothpicks
Prepared slides: amoeba and paramecium
Wright's stain

LAB 4

Prepared slide: onion root tip
Microscope
Optional:
    Onion roots
    Methylene blue
    Microscope slide: flat
    Cover slip
    Paper towel
    Dropper
    Water
    Sharp knife

LAB 5

Microscope
Prepared slides: amoeba and paramecium
Protist culture (mixed)
  *see note on p. 24 to prepare
Microscope slide: depression
Cover slips
Methyl cellulose (slowing agent)

LAB 6

Microscope
Microscope slides: flat
Cover slips
Prepared slide: zea mays (monocot stem or leaf cross-section)
Scalpel
Iodine
Methylene blue
Potato
Celery
Lettuce leaf
Onion
Carrot

LAB 7

Microscope
Prepared slides: monocot and dicot leaf cross-section

LAB 8

Microscope
Prepared slides: monocot and dicot stem cross-section
Microscope slide: flat
Celery
Methylene blue

LAB 9

Microscope
Prepared slide: root tip - long section
Prepared slide: root tip - cross section
Gelatin
Ruler

LAB 10

Microscope
Microscope slide: depression
Cover slip
Fresh flower with pollen (ex. lily or daffodil)
Petroleum jelly
Sugar water

LAB 11

Microscope
Clam
Cover slip
Dissection kit
Dissection pan
Knife with thick blade
Pins
Slides

LAB 12

Earthworm
Dissection kit
Dissection pan

LAB 13

Grasshopper
Dissection kit
Dissection pan

LAB 14

Fish
Dissection kit
Dissection pan

LAB 15

Fetal Pig: preserved
Dissection kit
Dissection pan
Long pins

LAB 18

Ruler
Stopwatch
Notebook

LAB 19

Watch with second hand
Graph paper
Three pound weight

1 | Record Keeping: Notebooks & Reports

The biologist must always have a record of the experiments, procedures, and data which he/she has completed. It is imperative that there be some sort of record in order to verify the experiment or the observations. The same is true for the student. The write-up of an experiment will show to others whether the student has understood the process and can draw conclusions from the data.

The notebook of the biologist can take various forms depending upon the type of data recorded. Likewise, the notebook of the student can vary according to the requirements of the instructor, the student, and/or the data.

In a laboratory write-up, there must be an **objective** or a question, or a **problem statement**. The student should be able to state that question. (so, should the teacher) There is always a reason for the experiment.

Some students have difficulties with identifying the **problem** in biological laboratories. This is because a lot of biology is simply observing and then drawing conclusions about the observations. This is no less good science than an experiment with controls and variables. A biologist must know what happens before attempting to alter a variable. So, for the problem statement, you may have a question to answer, a puzzling problem, or an unknown bit of data you wish to determine. It is OK to have as a problem statement: I intend to observe and draw the cellular structure of a muscle. It is not OK to write: To write up lab 37.

The **research** step for a biology laboratory experiment is really to read your text on the topic. Your instructor may require more and should if you are interested in this field. In your write-up, you can list the pages you read for this preparation, or you can briefly summarize the literature in the field.

The **hypothesis** is just your guess on the outcome of the experiment. If you do not have an experiment with variables, then you do not need to make a guess. If you are testing some physical response to a stimulus, like the speed of contracting your biceps, then you can guess about your success rate, or whether you can beat someone else's record.

The **procedure** of the experiment is what you did and how you did it. In this way another person (or you) can find a cause for an error in the experiment. Another reason for recording an exact procedure is that a scientist must be able to ensure reproducibility of the results.

If you are running an experiment, just describe what you did.

If you are using a procedure you found in another book, you must detail exactly your steps so that the experiment can be reproduced.

Another way of fulfilling this step is to draw a picture of what you did and how you set up the equipment.

The **data** collected is best shown in a chart, but may be written out. Observations in the form of drawings should be done according to the rules following this discussion. These rules are very old and drawings made from them are accurate, easy to read, and are recognizable. (Even for those like me who cannot draw.)

Calculations may not be necessary for every laboratory, but should go after the data if you have them. Charts are good here for recording the results of the calculations.

The **conclusion** step is very important. You must not leave it out because this is the step which reveals what, if anything, you have learned by doing this experiment. You will explain why it happened in this step. Or, maybe you will explain why you think it happened. Both are OK. This is also the place to ask more questions. Perhaps this experiment has been done many times before. If this is true, so be it. It can still lead YOU to ask more questions. Maybe some of THEM have not been asked before.

NOTEBOOK GUIDELINES:

1. Keep your reports in a notebook. This will allow you to add pages.

2. Each experiment will require about two or three pages. The ones which have drawings will be longer.

3. Keep each experiment together with the drawings you have made. Extra drawings like the traditional microscope drawing or others you make on your own for extra credit should be kept in a separate divider.

4. At the top of the page be sure to fill in your headings: name and date.

If you follow these guidelines you will have an accurate, neat, and handsome notebook.

MAKING GOOD LAB DRAWINGS

When you need to convey a message with descriptions, it is helpful to use drawings. A written passage may be ambiguous while a drawing is much more clear. You will find that there is a standard way to make a biological lab drawing. This method is the time-honored, traditional method of organizing the drawings. If you think that this is a waste of time, remember that for those of us who are not natural artists, this is a good way to create an easily-understood picture.

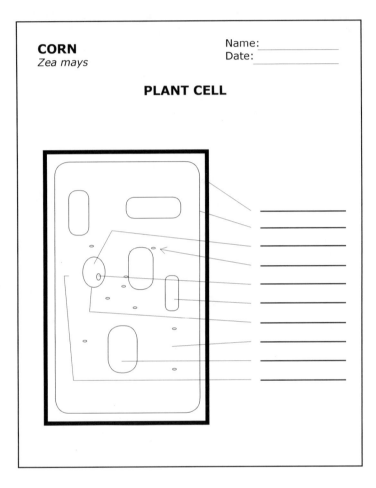

CORN
Zea mays

Name:
Date:

PLANT CELL

1. Draw the object making use of the entire drawing area with definite margins (for example: 1 inch) on all sides.

2. Leave the right-hand area for labels. I see no reason why a left-handed person cannot reverse this standard and label the drawing on the left.

3. Put an appropriate title at the top (or bottom) of the drawing. Print the words. (using all capitals is best). Draw a line first and write the letters on it if you have difficulty writing in a straight line (a common problem).

4. Label your drawing with the correct heading including name, date, species, sample medium (like: *hay infusion*), and the location of the specimen (if it is a field drawing).

5. On the right, opposite the part you will be labeling, draw a line. You will print the name of the part on this line. Capitalize the label.

6. Take your ruler and draw a straight line from the part to its label, crossing no other lines in the process.

7. If you must, instead of crossing a line, make a broken line leading to the label.

8. The end of the line which meets the part being labeled should end in an uncluttered, empty section of the part.

9. If the part is very small, use an arrow to point to the part.

10. If you are labelling several parts, use a bracket and end the line at the point of the bracket.

11. Do not add parts which you have not seen but assume to be present. Even if those parts are in the drawing in your book, you must not put them in your drawing unless you *actually* see them. This is part of the honor code of a scientific investigator.

BIOLOGY

Name:_____

Date:_____

Phylum_____

Class _____

Order_____

Family _____

Genus _____

species _____

Scientific Name _____

Common Name _____

USING THE MICROSCOPE

Your text probably has a section which includes the use of the microscope, but for the sake of completeness, I will include a few comments on the use of this valuable instrument.

Ever since Leeuwenhoek checked out the organisms living in a drop of water with his hand held microscope, biologists have been using this instrument. If you have access to an instrument, there are a few rules which you should know before you begin. No matter what the size of your scope, you should follow these rules.

1. Holding a microscope is not difficult, but you must force yourself to use **two** hands. One hand should be holding the arm. The other should be supporting the base.

2. There are **two lenses** which you will be looking through. The first is in the eyepiece. This is usually a 10X power lens which means that it magnifies an object ten times the original size.

The second is the objective lens piece. There are usually at least two objectives on student microscopes. One of these is 10X, and the other 43X power.

The total magnification is just the eyepiece's power multiplied by the objective len's power. So, you most probably have 100X power and 430X power.

If you have a more advanced microscope, you may have a 1000X power available, (although it is probably an oil immersion lens.)

Some microscopes have a 15X eyepiece so they will have 150X power and 860X power available for use.

3. A good scope is **para focal**. This means that when you focus the object with one objective lens, you will be able to turn the **nosepiece** and the higher power lens will be automatically in focus. This is really an advantage because high power can be difficult to focus.

4. The light you will be seeing through the microscope has a light path it must follow. The light will bounce off the **mirror** (or come from the light source under the stage), go through the **diaphragm**, then the hole in the stage, into the objective lens, through the **body tube**, and up through the eyepiece into your eye. You will need to align the mirror so that the light will follow this path. *Note: If you use sunlight, do not use a direct path for the light source. Use indirect light.*

5. The traditional way to learn to use the instrument is to cut out an "e" from the newspaper and mount it on a slide. Add one drop of water and then a cover slip. Put the slide cover-slip side up, on the stage over the hole. Use the stage clips to secure the slide.

6. Using the coarse adjustment, while looking at the objective lens and the slide from the outside of the microscope, lower the tube until the objective lens is almost touching the cover slip. Now, look through the eyepiece. You will probably see a shadow where the "e" is. Slowly raise the body tube until the "e" is in focus.

7. You can move the diaphragm knob so that the light grows dimmer or gets brighter. For some specimen, you will get better contrast with less light shining through it.

8. Adjust the focus even more closely by using the fine focus knob. You will not have to make very large movements to see a difference. When you use the fine focus, notice that you can see the upper surfaces of the "e", and then the lower surfaces.

9. To use a higher power, turn the nosepiece until the 43X power objective lens is in position. Watch from the outside while you do this because the high power lens can go lower than the slide's top surface. It is easily possible to break your slide this way.

If the microscope is para focal, you probably will not have to adjust the focus now. If you need some fine adjustment, use only the fine adjustment knob. Make the correction very carefully. If the lens must come down, watch it from the outside as before, then adjust the fine focus upward while you look through the eyepiece.

PARTS OF THE MICROSCOPE

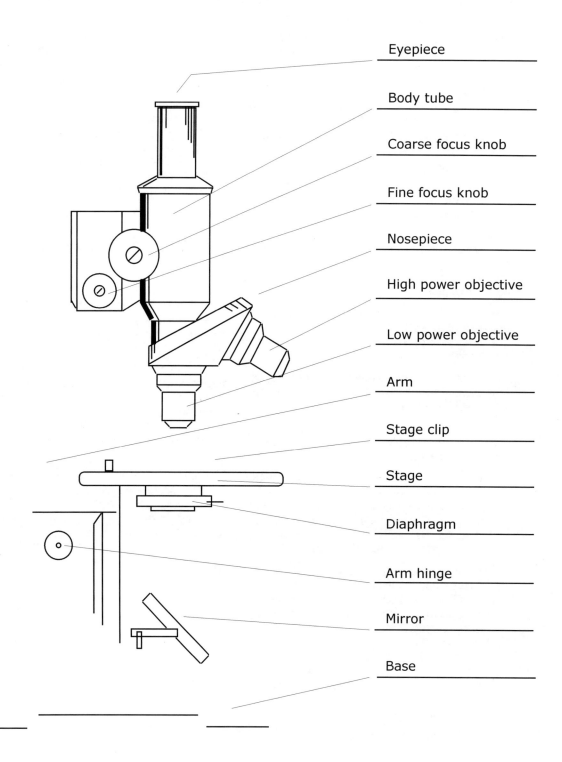

Eyepiece _____

Body tube _____

Coarse focus knob _____

Fine focus knob _____

Nosepiece _____

High power objective _____

Low power objective _____

Arm _____

Stage clip _____

Stage _____

Diaphragm _____

Arm hinge _____

Mirror _____

Base _____

PARTS OF THE MICROSCOPE QUIZ

Name:_____
Date:_____

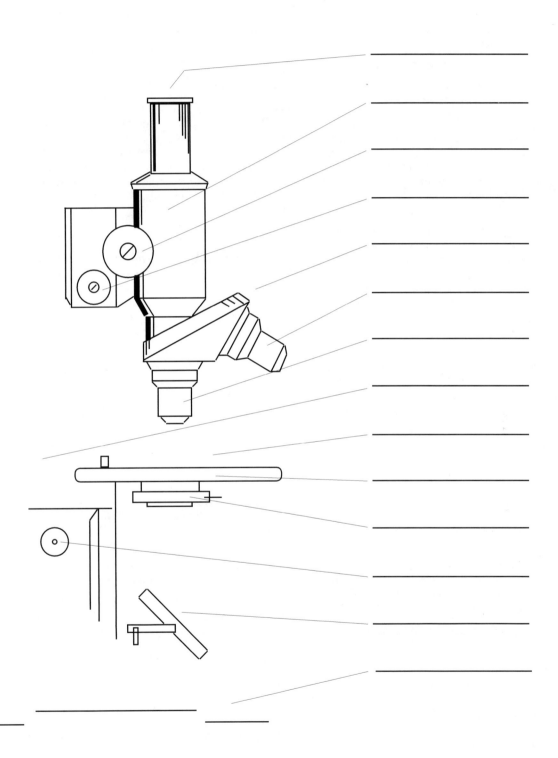

THE SCIENTIFIC METHOD

In a high school biology course you will use the scientific method for two reasons: for your science fair project and for your laboratory notebook.

The following paragraphs discuss the use of the scientific method and its use in a science fair project. On the page, The Biology Notebook, the use of the scientific method as the format of the lab reports is explained.

Science fair projects and the scientific method:

If a scientist is going to do serious and hopefully original research in science, she/he would use some variation of this set of steps. Obviously, a research report will not include all of these every time, so this is a generalized set of steps. But these are the steps usually used.

This long list is not some form of advanced torture designed for scientists. On the contrary, once a scientist has an interesting question, these steps are all very intriguing, especially if she/he has stumbled onto something no one has done before. A scientist would probably only use a list of this type so that she/he would not forget some vital step before publication. Half-done research is no research at all.

As a high-school student, a good project is one which includes at least some attempt at all of these. **I have seen original research get overlooked in science fairs because the student's use of the scientific method was not clear.**

Because of the nature of the judging, the scientific method has become an idealized concept, an end in itself. A project can be original, complete, and very nicely done but still not do well at a science fair, if the student does not know and use this set of steps. Plus, she/he must be very clear about her/his use of them.

Some states require additional steps, like a list of acknowledgements. Do not forget them if you wish to do well in the contest. Also, do not leave steps out just because they are not listed in the science fair handbook.

The oral part of the science fair is usually designed to discover if the student knows her/his experiment and if she/he knows and has used the scientific method. I suggest that you make a point of using the steps in your oral presentation, as well as the words "**control**" and "**experimental set-up**". You may have done everything quite well, but not win an award if you do not remember that in science fairs *communication* is the key word.

I have included this commentary so that the student may not be overwhelmed at a science fair. If you are aware of these things beforehand, you can systematically accomplish the steps required for a good score.

Step by Step

The **problem step** is only a statement, a simple sentence or two describing the question you tried to answer. Just writing down the problem is sometimes a real ordeal because it actually sums up what you have attempted to do with your entire experiment. Even though this step may be difficult, it is very important because it forces the student to organize his/her thoughts. This organization will be good for the rest of the project.

The **research step** is very important. It prepares you to do the experiment. By consulting experts, you learn more about your topic in a very painless way. Interviews are very nice ways of getting information. The telephone can be the means to really update your research step.

After you have learned something about your topic, you should be able to take a guess about the outcome of the experiment. This guess is your **hypothesis.**

Next, you start with a list of **materials** and a **procedure**. Many times one will follow the other as you concoct some type of setup you need for the experiment. It is normal for a student to have to change part of the experimental set-up. Say, for example, a piece of equipment is too expensive, so you build one. No problem. You don't have a balance scale, so you set up one using fishing string and weights. It still works.

The next step, **observations**, is easy to understand. The hard part is recording everything. I'll say that again, **record everything.**

The next four steps usually go together for the high school science fair or paper. You have the calculations you must make, and the answers you got from the calculations. These steps are the **calculation step** and the **result step**. If you do not have any calculations to make then you will not have these steps.

The **statistical analysis step** is the step which allows you to discover whether your results mean anything or not. You may have a large percentage error. This can mean a problem in the experimental set-up, or it may only indicate that you dropped something and used the data anyway. If the percentage error in your experiment is 25%, you might consider evaluating the sources of error since this is a very large number.

If the difference in two findings is not statistically different then you must consider them as very nearly the same number. For example, you have ten numbers: 2, 4, 7, 4, 1, 4, 4, 8, 9, 9.2. The 9 and 9.2 are within the same order of magnitude when compared to the other numbers. You may be able to round the 9.2 to 9. Of course, in this case, I would have to ask why your readings do not have the same number of significant digits.

You do this step when you have made calculations or have numerical findings.

Everyone who has done a science project needs a **sources of error step**. This is because every experiment has some error built into it. In order to make your experiment as complete as possible, you should think about these errors which crop up. During the experiment, you must try to reduce the effects of the errors, and after the experiment you must list the ones which still remain. It may be that you live in an area which does not require this step, but no really good experiment would be complete without it.

I have noticed that perfectly normal students often have a problem distinguishing between results and conclusions. The result of the experiment shows literally what happened and the answers to very specific calculations.

THE SCIENTIFIC METHOD STEPS ARE:
1. Statement of the problem
2. Research of the literature on the topic
3. Hypothesis
4. Materials list
5. Procedure used
6. Observations
7. Calculations
8. Results
9. Statistical analysis
10. Sources of error
11. Conclusions
12. Possibilities for future research

2 | Diffusion-Osmosis

MATERIALS

Carrots or Potatoes   Distilled water
Knife   Scale
Glasses (3)   Fruit
Salt or Sugar   Bowl
Plastic wrap

A cell is surrounded by a semi-permeable membrane. This means that the cell membrane will allow some things to pass through it and not others. It is semi-permeable.

One of the substances which will pass through it is water, distilled water. The passage of water through the membrane is regulated by the substances in the water.

Some nutrients are actively transported by the cell through the membrane. These are carried through minute holes in the cell membrane. This process is controlled by the cell. Hence the name, active transport. The diffusion of water across the semi-permeable membrane is called osmosis and is more or less automatic. The water will move in a certain direction across the membrane.

The direction of the movement of water through the semi-permeable membrane is dependent upon concentrations of salts, sugar, or other solute in the water on one side of the membrane. Water will move into the side which has the greater concentration of solute.

In an animal cell, the cytoplasm has more salt than a surrounding medium of distilled water. Yet, the same type of cell will have less salt than a surrounding medium of salty water. When a cell is surrounded by distilled water, it will tend to gain water from the surrounding medium. When the cell is suspended in salty water, it will lose water from inside the cell.

The following experiment shows an example of osmosis.

Procedure:

1. Cut up into slices a carrot or a potato. Put several slices into a glass which has been already weighed. Do this with three glasses. Record the weight of the slices in each cup.

2. Add distilled water to **Cup 1**. Cover **Cup 2** with a piece of plastic wrap and put on a rubber band so that the slices are sealed in. Into **Cup 3**, put salt water. Make the water so salty that there is salt on the bottom of the cup.

3. After letting the cups sit for several hours, empty them, drying out the insides. Pat the slices dry and return them to the cups. Make sure that the salt is all out of the Cup 3.

4. Re-weigh the cups and record the results.

5. Subtract the two weights. Did the slices gain, lose, or stay the same in weight?

Critical Thinking:

1. What is your hypothesis as to the slices in Cups 1, 2, & 3? Will they lose, gain, or stay the same in weight?

_____

_____

_____

_____

_____

2. What happened to the slices? Did the passage of water into or out of the slices conform to your hypothesis?

_____

_____

_____

_____

_____

_____

_____

_____

_____

Osmosis: Diffusion of water molecules across a semi-permeable membrane.

3. The growth of bacteria requires water as well as nutrients. What would you hypothesize would happen to bacteria which had nutrients but no water to live in?

_____

_____

_____

_____

_____

4. There are several food preservation techniques which deprive the bacteria of water. When we use salt to cure meats and sugar to preserve fruits and meats, we make use of this technique. Why do you think that jelly recipes stipulate that you must not reduce the amount of sugar required by the recipe? What might be the result?

_____

_____

_____

_____

_____

5. If the field in which you are planting your crops had a lot of salt in it, what would be the result on the germinating seeds? Look up the destruction of the fields of Carthage by the Roman Empire after Hannibal's attempted conquest. What the Romans did has long been the classic example of long term destruction of an enemy.

_____

_____

_____

_____

_____

6. Some people put salt on the sidewalk cracks to get rid of weeds. Comment upon this use of salt. What is happening and why is this not a good method to kill weeds?

_____

_____

_____

_____

_____

7. Put some fresh fruit in a bowl. Add about a cup of sugar. After an hour, what has happened and why?

_____

_____

_____

_____

_____

_____

DIFFUSION - OSMOSIS

Name:_____
Date:_____

CUP 1

Contents (Slices): _____ Beginning Weight: _____ Ending Weight: _____

Liquid: _____ Difference? _____

Loss or Gain? _____

Percentage Gained or Lost: _____

(Difference) ÷ (Beginning Weight) x 100% = % Gained or Lost

CUP 2

Contents (Slices): _____ Beginning Weight: _____ Ending Weight: _____

Liquid: _____ Difference? _____

Loss or Gain? _____

Percentage Gained or Lost: _____

(Difference) ÷ (Beginning Weight) x 100% = % Gained or Lost

CUP 3

Contents (Slices): _____ Beginning Weight: _____ Ending Weight: _____

Liquid: _____ Difference? _____

Loss or Gain? _____

Percentage Gained or Lost: _____

(Difference) ÷ (Beginning Weight) x 100% = % Gained or Lost

3 | General Cell Structure in Animals

MATERIALS

Alcohol
Distilled water
Iodine
Methylene Blue
Microscope
Microscope slides:
  flat
Cover slips

Needle
Paper toweling
Round toothpicks
Prepared slides:
  amoeba and
  paramecium
Wright's stain

The characteristics of the cells of animals are, of course, dependent on the function of that cell within the organism. Because of this, animal cells are not all alike, but are specialized.

However, there are certain features of animal cells which are characteristic. Some of these characteristic features are also present in plant cells, like cell membranes and nuclei. Others may be present in animal cells only, for instance, flagellae.

WARNING!!

Do not use these human tissue slide preparations if your school is not a family home school. You will understand that in the current crisis with the HIV and associated viruses, preventing transmission must be the teacher's foremost concern in the biology classroom.

During this laboratory, you will identify some of the structures which occur within the animal cell.

CHEEK CELLS

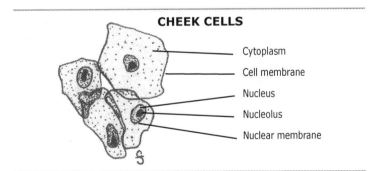

— Cytoplasm
— Cell membrane
— Nucleus
— Nucleolus
— Nuclear membrane

Procedure:

1. Using a round-ended toothpick, gently scrape the inside of your cheek. The toothpick will pick up cheek cells.

2. Wipe the cells onto a glass microscope slide and cover with a cover slip. With a fingertip or a pencil eraser, carefully push down on the cover slip without breaking it. If your cover slip is glass, you are very likely to break it if you push more than just barely. This is a dry mount.

3. Place the slide on the stage of the microscope and focus using low power. After the scope is focused, you may switch to high power while looking directly at, not through, the objective lens. You should not have to refocus, but if you do, use these directions: **While looking directly at the bottom of the objective lens and the slide, carefully lower the lens until it is not quite touching the slide. Now, looking through the microscope, pull the objective back away from the slide using the fine adjustment knob. This will allow you to focus the slide without putting the objective lens right through it.**

4. Make a drawing of your observations. You will be able to see the cell membrane, the almost translucent cytoplasm, and perhaps, the nucleus. Place a drop of water on the edge of the cover slip so that the water is drawn under the slip. This is a wet mount. Do you see any of the organelles more clearly? If so, draw them again, labeling the drawing as to the type of mount you have used.

5. Place a drop of iodine on the edge of the cover slip. Use a piece of a paper towel to draw the stain through the material under the cover slip. To do this put an edge of the paper towel next to the cover slip. Because of the absorbency of the towel, the stain will be drawn through towards the towel and in the process stain the cells in its path.

6. This stain will color the nucleus and the nucleolus. The nucleus will be the round or oval shaped structure within the cell that is darkly stained. The nucleolus will be an even more darkly stained area within the nucleus.

7. Draw a small group of cells which will show the general shape and arrangement of the cheek cells. Draw a representative cell above or beneath the group and label its organelles which you have been able to identify. Also present but more difficult to see are: **mitochondria, golgi bodies, endoplasmic reticula, ribosomes**, and **lysosomes**.

SQUAMOUS EPITHELIAL CELLS
(such as cheek cells)

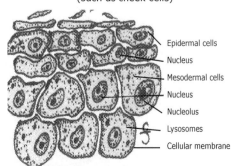

— Epidermal cells
— Nucleus
— Mesodermal cells
— Nucleus
— Nucleolus
— Lysosomes
— Cellular membrane

8. Paramecium or amoeba.: Change slides to the paramecium or amoeba slide and view under low power, then high power.

9. Make a group drawing of several of the cells. Then draw one cell labeling its parts. View under higher power in order to see the parts more clearly. Be very careful to keep from cracking the slide by moving the objective lens down only while looking directly at the objective and slide.

BLOOD CELLS
(optional)

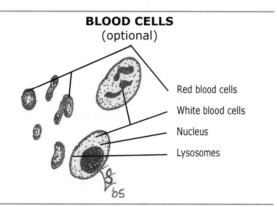

- Red blood cells
- White blood cells
- Nucleus
- Lysosomes

---

10. Blood cells: After washing your hands and wiping the tip of a finger with an alcohol prep, prick the finger tip and squeeze a bit of blood onto a glass slide. Hold another slide at a 45⁰ angle and push the drop of blood across the slide, making a smear. Let the slide dry.

11. Put two drops of Wright's stain on the blood smear and let it sit for a minute or two. Gently swish the slide in a container of distilled water. Do not hold under the running faucet. Let it dry again.

12. Without using a cover slip, observe under high power. Notice that the most numerous cells (the red ones) do not possess nuclei. Some of the white cells will appear to have several nuclei. Make drawings of both types of cells.

13. The white cells, or lymphocytes, have inclusions of different colors within the cells. They may also have visible lysosomes. The lysosomes contain very strong enzymes which break down bacteria, other body invaders, and worn out cell components.

14. On the slide with the cheek cells and on the drop of blood, add one drop each of methylene blue. This should stain the mitochondria of the cells. To the blood slide add a cover slip and observe. Draw the stained cells and the mitochondria, if possible.

Organelles not observed in the cells of this experiment, but which may be part of certain animal cells, especially those of free swimming organisms:

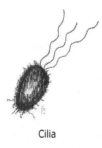

Cilia

Cirri (fused cilia)

Flagella

GENERAL CELL STRUCTURE IN ANIMALS

Critical Thinking:

1. Why do you think that biologists would need many different type of stains and staining techniques?

_____

_____

_____

2. Why do you think that the structures within the cells are called 'organelles'? Explain your answer.

_____

_____

_____

3. In the classification systems of the past one-celled animals have been described as 'simple organisms'. Why do you think that this may have been erroneous based upon what you have observed during this laboratory experience?

_____

_____

_____

4. Why might a cell from a multicellular organism be considered more simple than that of a one-celled organism?

_____

_____

5. Mitochondria are called the powerhouses of the cell. They metabolize food products to release energy. In what type of cell would you expect to see an increased number of mitochondria: cheek cells, muscle cells, bone cells, epithelial cells? Explain your answer.

_____

_____

6. You have seen several different shapes in animal cells. What is your hypothesis on the reasons for the different shapes?

_____

_____

7. The red blood cells do not have nuclei. What two important functions of the nuclei do not seem to be necessary to the red blood cells? Why?

_____

_____

_____

_____

_____

_____

8. Check the boxes below which describe the function(s) of the organelles on the left.

ORGANELLE	Protection	Support	Storage	Protein Synthesis	Transport In Cell	Reproduction	Energy Production	Waste Removal
Mitochondria								
Nucleus								
Vacuole								
Cell membrane								
Endoplasmic reticulum								
Ribosomes								
Centrioles								
Cytoplasm								
Nucleolus								
Golgi apparatus								

FUNCTION

ANIMAL CELLS

Name:

Date:

CHEEK CELLS

TYPICAL ANIMAL CELLS

BLOOD CELLS

4 | Reproduction: Cellular

MATERIALS

Prepared slide:
  onion root tip
Microscope
Optional:
  Onion roots
  Methylene blue
  Sharp knife

Microscope slide:
  flat
Cover slip
Paper towel
Dropper
Water

Growth within the plant is dependent upon a process called mitosis, cellular division. The plant does not just elongate or thicken its cells. While these processes do occur, true growth takes place because of mitosis.

A cell, after reaching a certain size and developmental stage, divides into two daughter cells. The division process usually takes about twenty minutes. In meristematic tissue, divisions take place which produce undifferentiated cells which will mature into the different tissue types of the plant. Plant tissue (a piece of a plant) can become undifferentiated during stress and can grow into another whole plant. This is the basis for vegetative cloning. Normally, however, growth occurs in the meristematic tissue which is located in the root tips, along the stem at the nodes and at the tip, the apical meristem.

You will look at the root tips of the onion for cell division. You will be able to see all the stages of mitosis. **You must remember, however, that the cell does not grow by separate stages. The series of stages are only called that by scientists. They actually form a process which is continuous without breaks or stages.**

Procedure:

1. Set up your microscope and focus it upon the prepared slide of the onion root tip.

2. Find examples of the six stages of mitosis and draw them, labeling the parts listed in the box below. Look in your text or in a reference (The Cell by Time-Life is an example.)

3. You can prepare your own slide showing the stages of mitosis by getting some root tips from an onion or carrot.

4. On a slide, gently smash and smear the tips. Add a drop or two of water and cover with the cover slip.

5. Stain with methylene blue by dropping a drop of the dye on one side of the cover slip and drawing the dye through with a paper towel.

6. Observe at low power to find some good cells, then change to high power. Make drawings of the dividing cells. Try to identify as many parts as you can.

"Bring out every kind of living creature that is with you — the birds, the animals, and all the creatures that move along the ground — so they can multiply on the earth and be fruitful and increase in number upon it."
Genesis 8:17

Centrioles
Cell wall
Centromere
Chromosomes
Chromatids
Membrane
  (reforming)
Nucleolus
Nucleus
Spindle

REPRODUCTION: CELLULAR

Name:_____

Date:_____

CRITICAL THINKING:

1. The total number of chromosomes in the prophase stage is:_____? If you cannot count them, assume them to be *x* number in the adult plant.

_____

_____

2. Why is this the necessary number during reproduction? How was this number achieved?

_____

_____

_____

_____

_____

3. What environmental factors will affect the successful reproduction of the chromosomes within the nucleus of the cell? What raw materials are needed? What would occur should the raw materials not be enough for reproduction? (Think of the make-up of the nucleic acids).

_____

_____

_____

_____

_____

_____

THE PHASES OF MITOSIS

Name:_____

Date:_____

Draw and label in the appropriate order.

Anaphase

Telophase

Metaphase

Interphase

Prophase

Specimen name: _____

Type of mount: _____

Type of stain: _____

5 | Protista: The Protozoans

MATERIALS
Microscope
Prepared slides: amoeba and paramecium
Protist culture (mixed)
  *see note on p. 24 to prepare
Microscope slide: depression
Cover slips
Methyl cellulose (slowing agent)

The study of microscopic life does not only refer to animals, but to all those things which live in the scale of a drop of water. These can be one-celled plants or animals, or they may not be one-celled at all. Some of these small organisms can be easily classified into a group, for example, a mayfly larva is one of the arthropoda. Others, however, classify with difficulty as the definitions we use with larger life forms are pulled down to the smaller scale. Sometimes this works; sometimes it does not.

There are strange organisms which possess features of both plants and animals. That is, they move and make food from light using chlorophyll or a similar pigment. How should these be classified? The Protista Kingdom is an attempt of solve the dilemma. As well, some scientists just avoid the whole question and concern themselves with the organisms and not their classification.

Note: "protist" = "protozoan"

PROTOZOAN: AMOEBA.

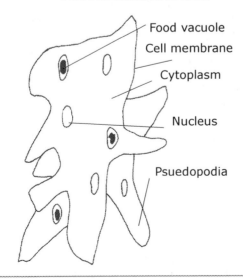

Food vacuole
Cell membrane
Cytoplasm
Nucleus
Psuedopodia

In this section of the manual, you will look at some animal-like protists. Later, you will look at some plant-like protists, the phytoplankton, and still later, you will have a chance to observe them all together in their more normal habitat.

The mixed culture of protists should have at least five types of protozoans within it. You might have available a copy of How To Know The Protozoa in order to identify the individuals. This helpful book can be found at a library. Or, you can find images online.

Procedure I:

1. Look at your prepared slide of _Amoeba proteus_ under low power with your microscope.

2. This is an organism which was long considered to be very simple. The cellular membrane is flexible and is capable of projecting out into the surrounding medium. These projections of membrane and cytoplasm are called pseudopods, or false feet. The organism can propel itself by extruding cytoplasm which has been anchored to the substrate and then by pulling the rest of its body towards the extended section of itself. Observe these pseudopods. Draw and label.

3. Notice the presence of nuclei. Some organisms may have more than one. Can you see any nucleoli?

4. Observe the slide of paramecium. These organisms are much faster in real life and are propelled by the beating of their cilia, small hair-like projections on the surface of their membranes. The paramecium spins as it swims and uses the currents set up by the forward motion to capture food. The food goes into the oral groove and then into the gullet. This food is usually bacteria. Amoeba will feed on paramecium and this parasitic relationship has been the basis for many experiments on parasitism.

Cilia move in rhythmic cycles, controlled by nerve-like organelles within the paramecium.

5. Draw a representative organism of each of your example types. Label these parts for the amoeba: **Cell membrane, cytoplasm, nucleus, nucleolus, vacuoles: food and waste, pseudopods.** Label these parts for the paramecium: **Cell membrane, cytoplasm, vacuoles: food, waste and contractile, cilia, gullet, oral groove, micronucleus and macronucleus.**

VORTICELLA: EXTENDED FORM

When digesting food within bell-shaped cavity, vorticella is contracted.

Rock or other support

Procedure II:

NOTE: If you do not have the mixed culture of the protists, you can use a hay infusion which has matured for 24 hours or so. This is a bit of hay submerged in some water. Add a little wheat or rice to encourage the growth of other protozoans.

1. Prepare a slide of the culture by placing one or two drops of the culture into the depression of a depression slide.

2. Add one drop of the protist slowing agent into the depression.

3. Put one edge of the slide cover into the mixture and slip the cover onto the depression so that the entire depression is covered.

4. Place on the microscope stage and observe, making drawings of your observations. Be sure to label all parts of the protozoans which you are able to identify. These drawings should go into your laboratory notebook. This page will also record your population statistics and behavior notes.

5. Estimate the size of the organism and record.

NOTE: *To estimate the size of your beastie, you make note of its size in comparison to the viewing field. When the microscope is on low power, the viewing field may be measured using a clear ruler. Bring the ruler into focus and read it. Record the diameter in millimeters. A micron is 0.001 mm.*

Knowing the length of the viewing field, you can estimate the size of the organism in comparison to the whole field. For example, one-quarter of the field. So, if the whole field is 325 microns, one-quarter of that would be about 81 microns.

Another way to figure it is to measure the organism with a clear scale which is slipped under the objective allowing a direct measurement of the organism. If you have measured the diameter of the viewing screen with a clear ruler. Assume that the whole screen is 1600 microns under low power, and the organism is 1/10th of the distance across the screen, then the organism is 160 microns long.

6. After you have looked around the slide for a good specimen to draw, count the number of similar organisms and record the approximate number. For some, you may only observe one sample while for others you will be unable to count them because of their great number. Do not let these circumstances dissuade you from attempting the counts. Record these numbers in the blanks available.

PARAMECIUM: FEEDING IN MOTION

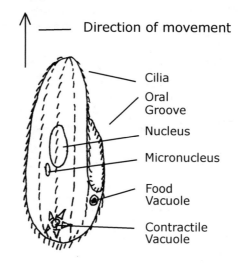

— Direction of movement

Cilia

Oral Groove

Nucleus

Micronucleus

Food Vacuole

Contractile Vacuole

PROTISTA: THE PROTOZOANS

Name:_____

Date:_____

Critical Thinking I:

1. Amoebas can be parasitic for humans. Look up *Entamoeba histolytica* for an example of a dangerous human parasite. This amoeba can encyst into a hardened capsule which even boiling will not harm. What is the usual method of prevention for this type of infestation?

_____

_____

_____

2. Look up the method of conjugation and draw an example of two paramecia conjugating and their resultant daughter cells.

_____

_____

Critical Thinking II:

1. Did you find nuclei within the single-celled organisms of your culture? Did any have multiple nuclei? What purpose could several nuclei serve in one cell?

_____

_____

2. Do you have paramecium? What seems to be their method of feeding? (If you do not have a paramecium, choose one which you do have in your culture.)

_____

_____

3. Does the amoeba have a similar method? Describe its method of feeding.

_____

_____

4. Are there any predators? Which are they?

_____

_____

5. How many different types of locomotion have you spotted?

_____

_____

_____

_____

Name:_____
Date:_____

ORGANISM: AMOEBA

CULTURE MEDIUM:_____

AMOEBA

ORGANISM: PARAMECIUM

CULTURE MEDIUM:_____

PARAMECIUM

Source of sample protozoans: _____

Location of sample collection: _____

Type of infusion: _____

Total population size: _____

Total number of different organisms: _____

Name:_____

Date:_____

1. Name: _____	2. Name: _____	3. Name: _____
Size:_____	Size:_____	Size:_____
Population count:_____	Population count:_____	Population count:_____
4. Name: _____	5. Name: _____	6. Name: _____
Size:_____	Size:_____	Size:_____
Population count:_____	Population count:_____	Population count:_____

6 Cell Structure: Plant

MATERIALS

Microscope
Microscope slides:
   flat
Cover slips
Prepared slide:
   zea mays
   (monocot stem
   or leaf cross-
   section)

Scalpel
Iodine
Methylene blue
Potato
Celery
Lettuce leaf
Onion
Carrot

Zea mays is corn, a major grain crop in the United States. This grass is monoecious meaning that both sexes are present on the one plant. The tassel produces the pollen and the ovary is located on the stalk in a part bearing the ear and silks.

There are two basic stages in the life of the corn plant. In the first, the photosynthetic products go mainly towards plant growth. In the second, the photosynthetic products go toward the production of the fruit.

Since the corn plant is a grass, the stem is not woody, but herbaceous. The stalk has vascular bundles distributed throughout its mass.

Look at the generalized plant cell drawing. All plant cells do not have every organelle. Some cells actually die and leave the cell wall only.

GENERALIZED PLANT CELL

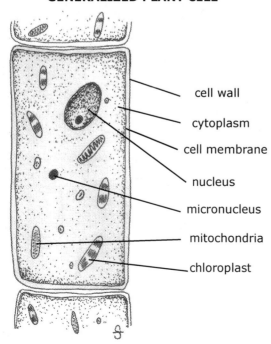

cell wall

cytoplasm

cell membrane

nucleus

micronucleus

mitochondria

chloroplast

Procedure I:

1. Set up the microscope and focus the zea mays (monocot stem or leaf cross-section) slide. Prepare your drawing paper.

2. Observe the individual cell types. Do you see several varieties? You should. Just as animals have tissues, (groups of like cells which perform specialized functions) so plants have different tissues. Draw a section of the stem of *Zea mays* and label those different types of cells.

3. The first and outermost layer of cells is the epidermis. You will note that the epidermis is only one layer. Do you observe any chloroplasts?

4. The next two or three layers are stained the same color. Are there any other cells stained the same color in the cross-section?

5. Notice the vascular bundles within the stem. Do most of them appear to be located in a certain area?

6. Draw a single vascular bundle. Label the **xylem**, the **vascular cambium**, and the **phloem.**

7. What type of cells are in the center of the stem? Notice the differences between the cells of the center and those of the outer edge. Attempt to justify these differences by function. Ask yourself: In what way does the plant use this type of cell in this location?

8. Complete your drawing, label, and shade if necessary. In this drawing a little touch of color to reflect the coloring of the stains would be appropriate.

9. One the most difficult things to do with a plant slide is to be able to visualize the slide in three dimensions, not just the two you see on the stage of the microscope. Try to do this. Now draw the vascular bundle lengthwise. Use arrows to show the movement of minerals, water, and sugar produced by the plant.

10. Which cells have the thickest cell wall? These are the cells which give the stalk its strength and support. You will note the absence of a skeleton of bones. The plant must still have support and this is the way it is designed. Be sure to label in your drawing the cells which have the thickened walls.

11. Under high power look for one or two cells and try to identify the organelles present. Try to find: nucleus, nucleolus, mitochondria, food vacuoles, and chloroplasts.

Procedure II:

1. Another way to observe the structure of the plant is to make your own wet mounts. Using a scalpel, or a razor blade, thin-slice cross-sections of plants. Suggested plants are the stem of celery, a leaf of lettuce, a bay leaf, a piece of a potato, the thin layer of an onion. There are many more possible plants you can use. Place the thin section on a slide with a drop of water. If you plan to use a stain, now is a good time. Remember, the stains are very strong so you only need a drop. Place a cover slip over the specimen to view.

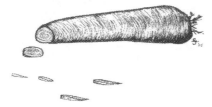

Note: A word of caution about these stains. They will easily stain your clothing or whatever they touch.

2. Celery: slice at an angle across the stem. This way you will get a very thin, one-cell layer on one edge. In the celery stem, you should be able to see nice vascular bundles distributed in the areas next to the outside of the stem. Use a drop of methylene blue for a stain.

3. Potato: The potato stores a lot of starchy food within the food vacuoles of the root. You can see this plainly under the microscope if you place one drop of iodine on the potato thin slice. It may be necessary to rinse the slice slightly before you can see light through the slice. The potato stores a lot of food and, when it is stained, it is quite dark unless the slice is very thin.

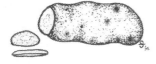

4. Leaf: When preparing a leaf, like lettuce, bend the leaf and tear it in half so that the leaf has a thin edge showing at the tear. Peel back the leaf and tear along the bend. In this way you will be able to see guard cells clearly. Try staining with methylene blue.

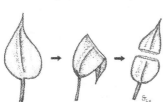 

5. Onion: The thin layer of tissue between the larger layers of the onion make an excellent study with the microscope. Using tweezers, pry apart one piece of the thin layer. Carefully place on a glass slide so that the tissue lies flat. Make sure that you get a torn section of the thin layer. Add a drop of water to your slide and carefully slide a cover slip onto the tissue. Observe under the microscope and make a drawing of one or two cells. Add one drop of methylene blue stain to one edge of the cover slip. Gently hold a piece of toweling to the opposite edge of the cover slip and draw the stain across the tissue sample. Observe under the microscope again, both low and high power. Make a drawing of your observations.

Critical Thinking:

1. Plant architecture deals with the structure of the plant as it relates to the tissues within the plant. Some cell types have strong, heavy cell walls and can provide the support necessary to withstand high winds. Others have holes in their ends which make them look like sieves and which function not for support but for water transport. Draw a cross-section which shows the areas of the stem with the strongest cell walls. Analyze the drawing and hypothesize as to the type of support structure the corn plant uses. If you have a corn plant, look on it for the adventitious supporting roots and cross-section one of them. Make sure to get a very thin layer. Take a look at it under your scope. Do not forget to make a drawing.

2. Where are the chloroplasts located in the stem of the corn plant? Verify this by cutting into a plant stem if you have a corn plant available. Why do you think that this is advantageous to the plant?

_____

_____

_____

_____

3. Most plants have a cuticle, or waxy layer, on the outer epidermis of the leaf. Why do you think this would help a plant? *Hint: Why do you cover things with plastic before putting them in the freezer?* Did your corn plant on the slide have a cuticle?

_____

_____

_____

_____

_____

_____

PLANT CELL STRUCTURE

Name:_____

Date:_____

Plant Name: _____

Type mount (Wet/Dry): _____

Stain used (if any): _____

CELL TYPES	FORM AND FUNCTION						
	Number of Nuclei	Chloro-plasts	Wall Size: Thick or thin	Function	Type of Nutrient Trans-ported	Food Storage	Other Function?
Epidermal cells							
Schlerenchyma							
Air space							
Vascular bundles							
Phloem							
Xylem							
Vacuoles							
Waxy layers							
Guard cells							

PLANT CELLS

Name:_____

Date:_____

Phylum_____

Class _____

Order _____

Family _____

Genus _____

species _____

Scientific Name _____

Common Name _____

PLANT CELLS

Name:_____

Date:_____

Phylum_____

Class _____

Order_____

Family _____

Genus _____

species _____

Scientific Name _____

Common Name _____

7 | Leaf Structure

MATERIALS
Microscope
Prepared slides: monocot and dicot leaf
    cross-section

The leaf is:

1. A chamber for the exchange of gases.

2. A place with large surface area for the process of photosynthesis.

3. The exit location for the process of transpiration in which water from the roots is transmitted to the atmosphere.

Because of all these things, leaves are very important to the plant. Also because of these functions, the leaf does not usually look like other parts of the plant. The specialization of function requires a designed-in specialization of form.

For example: The process of photosynthesis is dependent upon light. Usually, this means the more light the better for the plant. So, an increase in the surface area of the plant dependent on photosynthesis (the leaf) would be beneficial for the plant. The leaf is admirably designed for the absorption of light, especially the broad-leafed plants.

Procedure:

1. Take out the microscope and the leaf slides: monocot and dicot.

2. Prepare your drawing papers, one for each leaf type.

3. Make drawings of each leaf, labeling the component parts including: **stomata, guard cells, palisade layer, spongy layer, lower epidermis, upper epidermis, cuticle, vascular bundles, phloem, air space, xylem, mid rib, chloroplasts.**

4. Take a leaf of Ligustrum, _Ficus benjimina,_ or lettuce. Bend the leaf without breaking it and tear it in such a way that the lower epidermis of the leaf is exposed in a thin layer. Place this on a slide, add one or two drops of water, and cover with a cover slip. Place under the microscope and observe under low power then higher power. Make careful drawings of the leaf structures.

5. Observe the guard cells of the stomata and the regular formation of the epidermal layer cells.

6. Observe an open stomate and a closed one, checking for differences between the two. You can draw salt water across the slide in order to close the stomata. distilled water to open them.

Critical Thinking:

1. What is the formula for photosynthesis?

2. When herbivores eat plants, they must be able to grind up the plant tissue with their teeth. Why is this grinding necessary to the absorption of the plant nutrients? What particular part of the leaf cell requires this action?

3. Because of the answer to question 2, what do you hypothesize about the shape of the teeth necessary to the plant eater, or herbivore?

4. There are two basic parts to the photosynthetic process: the light reaction and the dark reaction. It should be obvious that the light reaction requires light. The dark reaction takes place at night. Look up the two types of reactions and write them out here:

LEAF STRUCTURE

Name:_____

Date:_____

5. What gas is produced during the day and released through the stoma? What gas is produced and released during the night? Are they the same?

_____

_____

_____

6. What effect would the release of water have on the atmosphere surrounding the plant? Several countries have, in the recorded past, cut down all of their natural forests. The climate in the area has been made drier and has less rainfall. An example of this is Lebanon. Could you hypothesize that the cutting down of the trees affected the climate? Explain. Use references if possible.

_____

_____

_____

_____

_____

_____

_____

_____

7. What is the spongy layer? Do you think that there is a function in this form? What could it be?

_____

_____

_____

8. Pesticides sprayed upon the leaves of plants may have certain effects. One, the leaf may become poisonous. Do you think that the pesticide could be absorbed by the leaf? What could be the mechanism if the waxy layer protects the leaf from invasion?

_____

_____

_____

_____

9. The high absorption of gases and other substances through the leaves has other helpful uses to botanists and farmers. What would you hypothesize about sprayed-on fertilizer? Call your local agricultural extension agent to find out about the effectiveness of sprayed-on chemicals.

_____

_____

_____

_____

_____

Scientific Names:

    Monocot: _____

    Dicot: _____

Common Names of Plants:

    Monocot: _____

    Dicot: _____

Monocot—dimensions of leaf:

    length: _____

    width: _____

Dicot—dimensions of leaf:

    length: _____

    width: _____

Name: _____

Date: _____

Power magnification: _____

Title: _____

8 | The Cell Interior and Function

MATERIALS

Microscope
Prepared slides: monocot and dicot stem cross-section
Microscope slide: flat
Celery
Methylene blue

The stems of plants serve several functions: support for the leaves, separation of the leaves, corridor for the transportation of fluids and nutrients, both upwards and downwards.

The leaves of the plant form a heavy canopy which usually must be lifted off of the ground in order to get room for gas exchange and light reception. I say usually because there are nearly always exceptions to the norm in nature. The leaves are the main organ for photosynthesis and because of this need to be exposed to light. When the leaves are separated from each other in some systematic way, more light is received by each leaf.

The transportation of fluids and nutrients takes place within the stem. The vascular bundles of the herbaceous plants, both monocot and dicot provide this function. Woody plants have a very efficient transport system but rearrange the tissues which do the transporting.

Procedure:

1. Set up your microscope and focus the slide of the monocot stem.

2. You have probably seen the monocot stem before, since the type which is usually in these slides is *Zea mays*, corn. Do you notice the name, mays, and its similarity to maize, another name for corn? Once again, note the placement of the vascular bundles in the monocot. Draw and label the cross-section. You should color the cells.

3. Make a drawing of the dicot stem cross-section. Label the drawing according to the list in the box.

4. Each type of stem has phloem and xylem cells. Each type of stem has the same functions to perform: support for the plant leaves, transportation of water and nutrients upward from the roots, and produce starches from the leaves downward to the rest of the plant. These tissues are present in both dicot and monocot plants. Draw representative vascular bundles from each.

5. What evidence of mitosis can you find in either stem? Find the cambium layer between the phloem and xylem of the dicot stem. Label it in your drawings.

6. Look at the cross-section of a thin piece of celery. Is the stem representative of a monocot or a dicot based on its cell structure?

7. Look at the stem of a potato which has begun to grow with a microscope. Is this the stem of a monocot or a dicot?

MONOCOT STEM: *ZEA MAYS.*

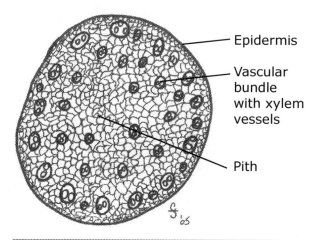

Epidermis

Vascular bundle with xylem vessels

Pith

PARTS TO IDENTIFY

Phloem
Xylem
Cambium
Epidermis
Pith
Vessel
Air space
Sclerenchyma
Vascular bundles

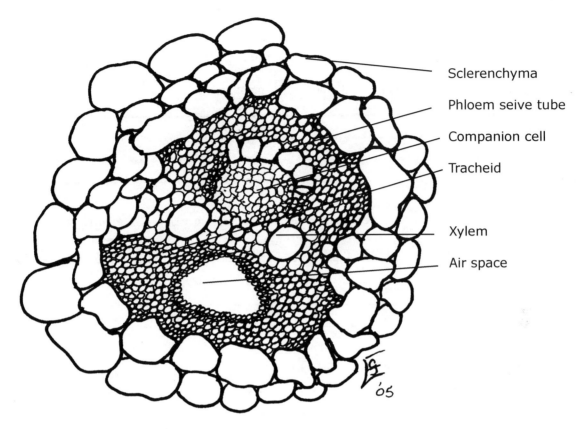

Sclerenchyma

Phloem seive tube

Companion cell

Tracheid

Xylem

Air space

MONOCOT VASCULAR BUNDLE: _____

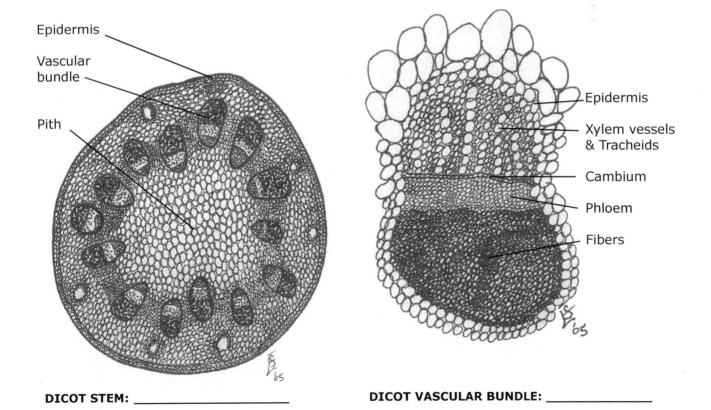

Epidermis

Vascular bundle

Pith

Epidermis

Xylem vessels & Tracheids

Cambium

Phloem

Fibers

DICOT STEM: _____   **DICOT VASCULAR BUNDLE:** _____

STEM STRUCTURE

Name:_____

Date:_____

Critical Thinking:

1. Why is there a need for both xylem and phloem in a plant stem?

_____

_____

_____

_____

2. In what ways is the herbaceous dicot stem that you studied more like a tree cross-section than is the monocot stem?

_____

_____

_____

_____

3. What is the similar outer layer of these plants?

_____

_____

And what role does it perform for each type of plant?

_____

_____

_____

4. Since aphids suck sap out of the plant, and they are very small insects, what part of the plant are they getting this sap from and what is it most likely to be made up of?

_____

_____

_____

_____

Monocot stem: _____

Monocot vascular bundle: _____

Dicot Stem: _____

Dicot vascular bundle: _____

9 Root Structure

MATERIALS

Microscope
Prepared slide: root tip - long section

Prepared slide: root tip - cross section
Gelatin
Ruler

The root of a plant has a structure which, like other plant parts, depends upon the functions it performs. You are already aware that the root must take in water and nutrients from the substrate. The root must anchor the plant against all weather conditions. There are aspects of these simple statements, though, that make impacts upon the structure of the root system which are not so simple.

1. The root is a meristem. That is, it is a growing location with undifferentiated cells.

2. Mitosis is taking place within the root tip.

3. This growth is going on through an abrasive medium requiring protection of the meristematic area, that is the growing areas. This protector is the root cap.

4. The amount of water which the root must absorb should be equal to the amount leaving the leaves. This is necessary to maintain the osmotic pressure within the plant, or the plant will wilt. Maintaining water pressure is one of the supporting mechanisms of the plant.

5. Remember that the leaves must have a large surface area for the reception of light. (Of course, this is only the usual case, certainly not a universal statement. Observe the pencil cactus whose stems do most of the photosynthesizing.) Over a lot of that surface area are stomates through which water passes. The root must have approximately a similar amount of area through which to absorb that water.

6. The answer to the surface area problem is root hairs. By having a small, thin volume, the relative amount of surface area is increased.

All of these things mentioned above impact what the root is going to look like under the microscope.

Surface area investigation:

1. Make up some stiff gelatin and cut it into three or four different sizes of cubes. Make them fairly large cubes.

2. Calculate the volumes of the cubes and fill in the blanks.

3. Now, calculate the surface areas of the cubes. Record these numbers.

4. Chart these values on graph paper. The horizontal axis should be the side length marked in evenly spaced increments (metric). The vertical axis should be the variable which is dependent upon the horizontal axis' number. In this case, the dependent variable is the surface area divided by the volume of the cubes. What kind of curve did you get?

Surface area/ volume (vertical axis)

Side length (horizontal axis)

Cube Number	Dimensions	Volume	Surface Area	Surface Area/Vol.

Procedure:

1. Get out your root tip slides, microscope, and drawing paper.

2. Make a drawing of the root tip under low power. This will get you oriented to the root and give you a chance to see some of the macro-features of the root.

Notice the **root cap**. The root cap is a protective structure of cells designed to slough off when abraded. It is very much like the heat shields of the Mercury capsules from the early space exploration days. The root tip has an advantage that the Mercury capsule did not have in that the cells are replaced as needed by the mitosis going on beneath the root cap.

The **root hairs** are the thin, little structures protruding from the sides of the root. These are the surface area increasing structures of the root. They are the primary places of water absorption for the plant. Imagine pulling up a seedling from the ground. The root hairs are very fragile and this type of action will tear them off of the root. What do you think will happen to the water absorbing capabilities of the plant once it is replanted? What will be the first item which the plant must replace?

3. Now change to high power. If your microscope is **parafocal** you will not have to readjust the focus. Now, you will start your second root drawing. Observe the different types of cells in the root. This is usually a fun slide to look at since you will see cells in nearly all stages of mitosis.

The **epidermis** is, of course, the outer layer or two of cells. Notice their shape. Do some of them seem to be brick-shaped? You should see a few with protusions from them. These are the origin of root hairs. Now, you can see the fragility of a single celled hair. Note the placement of nuclei.

The **apical meristem** or the growing region on the tip of the root is, as you saw before, behind the root cap. This is the location of the mitosis, or cell division going on in the root. After the cells divide, they are called undifferentiated cells. That is, they do not have their mature shape or function yet and, if transplanted, will develop into the type of cell the plant needs at that new location instead of the type into which it would have developed.

As you look further back down the root tip and away from the undifferentiated area, you will see the cortex which is a loosely organized area under the epidermis. This region is called the **region of elongation**. The reason for the name should be fairly clear. You should be able to see that the nuclei are farther apart.

Further away from the apical meristem are some different types of cell forms. The root hairs are present as well as the beginnings of the root vascular system.

The **stele, or primary vascular tissue** can be seen in the center region of the root.

4. In the drawing below, I have included a few structures which you may or may not be able to see in your slide, but which are still interesting.

The area of increasing differentiation will show the new root beginning to have a more mature form. Within the layer of cortex is the single layer of **endodermal cells** and within that is the **pericycle**, another layer of cells. Inside of these layers is the conducting **stele**, containing both **xylem** and **phloem**.

ROOT: LONG SECTION

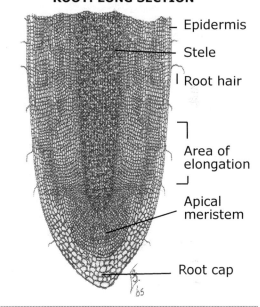

- Epidermis
- Stele
- Root hair
- Area of elongation
- Apical meristem
- Root cap

ROOT CROSS-SECTION

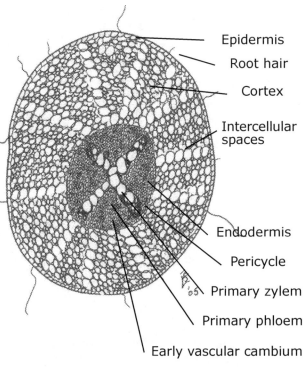

- Epidermis
- Root hair
- Cortex
- Intercellular spaces
- Endodermis
- Pericycle
- Primary zylem
- Primary phloem
- Early vascular cambium

ROOT STRUCTURE

Name:_____

Date:_____

CRITICAL THINKING:

1. When a tree is transplanted, what size of root ball should be dug up? Explain your answer.

_____

_____

2. Do the roots move? Explain the term *hydrotrophism* as it is used today.

_____

_____

3. What do you notice about the growth of plants directly under the leafy canopy of a tree? Do they thrive or are they stunted? Hypothesize more than one result of this position.

_____

_____

_____

4. In what way does the plant use the various tissues within the root? That is, what functions do the parts perform? Describe the xylem, phloem, root hairs, and epidermis.

_____

_____

5. Find a secondary root in your slide. Where does the growth originate? Hypothesize as to the origin of the meristematic tissue. This is a question which really has no correct answer as yet since the answer lies in the differentiation of the tissues in the root.

_____

_____

6. Name three foods from roots. From what part of the root did they develop?

_____

_____

LONGITUDINAL SECTION   **CROSS-SECTION**

Reproduction: 10 Pollen Germination

MATERIALS

Microscope
Microscope slide: depression
Cover slip

Fresh flower with pollen (ex. lily or daffodil)
Petroleum jelly
Sugar water

The pollen grain is a container for the male gamete of the plant. Pollen grains are formed on the anther and during pollination of the flower lands upon the stigma of the pistil. There is a sugary, sticky solution on this part of the pistil which causes the pollen to adhere to the pistil.

In the presence of this sugary water solution, the pollen sheath splits and the pollen germinates and begins to grow its pollen tube. This long tube grows down the pistil until it comes to the ovary and into contact with an egg. The pollen nuclear material travels down the tube and fertilizes the egg.

In this experiment, you will observe the beginning of pollen tube growth. This is called pollen germination. Pollen germination is not the same thing as seed germination, although the term is the same.

Procedure:

1. Trace around the depressed center of the depression microscope slide with petroleum jelly. This will form a protective layer around the pollen grains in the depression and prevent them from drying out.

2. Prepare a sugar solution (a few grains of sugar will be fine, or honey with water) and put a few drops on the depression slide.

DEPRESSION SLIDE

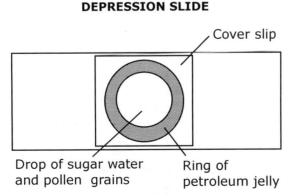

Cover slip

Drop of sugar water and pollen grains

Ring of petroleum jelly

3. Add a scattering of pollen grains on the depression, too. Put on a cover slip. Start timing the experiment.

4. Make a drawing of your slide under the microscope showing the pollen grains.

5. The pollen grains will swell within minutes (perhaps an hour). They will show signs of growth by becoming oblong shapes. This definite growth should appear within two hours, but I have seen longer responses. The length of time is dependent upon the development stage of the pollen (if it is ripe or not), the amount of sucrose in the water, and the type of pollen it is.

6. Make drawings every so often showing the growth of the pollen tubes.

7. Keep a record of the number of tubes growing in your slide.

8. Calculate the percentage germination of your pollen grains.

POLLEN GRAINS: GERMINATING

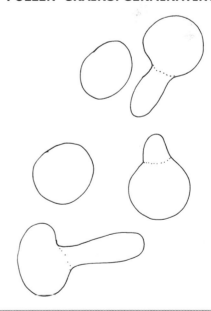

REPRODUCTION: POLLEN GERMINATION

Name:_____

Date:_____

Critical Thinking:

1. Most pollen is yellow. Why would you expect this to be the case? *Hint: Have you ever been stung by an insect while wearing yellow?*

_____

_____

2. Why do you think that pollen comes in so many different shapes?

_____

_____

3. How would you expect acid rain to affect the germination of the pollen grain? Try a little vinegar on it and see.

_____

_____

_____

_____

4. In what seasons does pollen usually fall? Certain types of pollen cause allergic reaction among people. How might this be avoided?

_____

_____

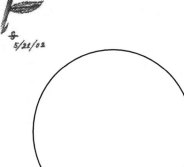

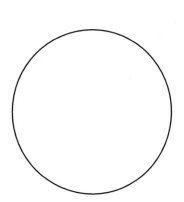   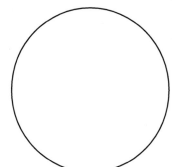

Time: 0 Hours   **Time: 2 Hours**   **Time: 4 Hours**

pollen grains: _____   # pollen grains: _____   # pollen grains: _____

pollen tubes: _____   # pollen tubes: _____   # pollen tubes: _____

germinating: _____   # germinating: _____   # germinating: _____

POLLEN GERMINATION

Name: _____

Date: _____

Type of Plant: _____

**DRAWINGS SHOWING THE GROWTH OF THE POLLEN TUBE
AFTER THE DESIGNATED LENGTHS OF TIME.**

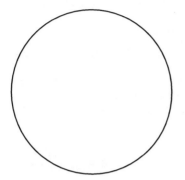
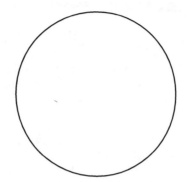
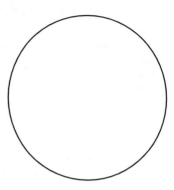

Time: 0 Hours

\# pollen grains: _____

\# pollen tubes: _____

\# germinating: _____

Time: 2 Hours

\# pollen grains: _____

\# pollen tubes: _____

\# germinating: _____

Time: 4 Hours

\# pollen grains: _____

\# pollen tubes: _____

\# germinating: _____

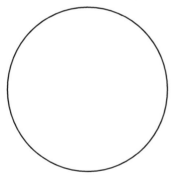
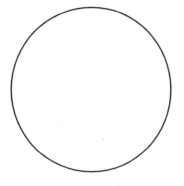
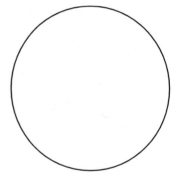

Time: 6 Hours

\# pollen grains: _____

\# pollen tubes: _____

\# germinating: _____

Time: 8 Hours

\# pollen grains: _____

\# pollen tubes: _____

\# germinating: _____

Time: 12 Hours

\# pollen grains: _____

\# pollen tubes: _____

\# germinating: _____

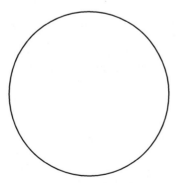
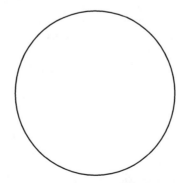
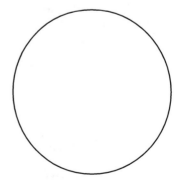

Time: 14 Hours

\# pollen grains: _____

\# pollen tubes: _____

\# germinating: _____

Time: 16 Hours

\# pollen grains: _____

\# pollen tubes: _____

\# germinating: _____

Time: 18 Hours

\# pollen grains: _____

\# pollen tubes: _____

\# germinating: _____

11 | Dissection: Clam

MATERIALS

Microscope	Dissection pan
Clam	Knife with thick blade
Cover slip	Pins
Dissection kit	Slides

The clam is a mollusk, a bivalve, and an aquatic organism. The fact that it is aquatic should lead you to expect that it has gills to extract the oxygen from the water. Since the gills are inside of the shells (two of them), you might expect that the shells are normally open while the organism is functioning as usual. These two suppositions are correct. The presence of gills and the need to keep the shells open are definitely related. The closing of the shells occurs during stress as in predation and while the organism is exposed to the atmosphere. In order to keep the shell closed the mollusk must have some large muscles. These attach to the shell at a specific distance from the hinge point. They are placed in such a way that the they have the advantage of a moderately long lever arm requiring less force than if the muscles were attached closer to the hinge line. The clam has many such elements in its design, so as you dissect this organism, think of the impact the environment has on the design. This attitude will give you a greater understanding into the relationship between form and function.

EXTERNAL VIEW OF THE CLAM:

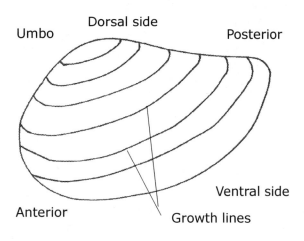

Exterior Structure:

1. Check the drawing of the external clam and find these parts on your clam. **Umbo, Growth lines, Anterior end, Posterior end, Dorsal, and Ventral sides**. The shell is made up of several parts. The **umbo** is the oldest part of the shell and you can see the progression of **growth rings** outward from it. The outer layer of the shell is the acid resistant **periostracum**. Why do you think this resistance to acids would be an advantage to the clam?

2. The next inner layer of shell is the **prismatic layer,** where calcium carbonate crystals are laid perpendicular to the outer layer. The innermost layer which lies next to the mantle is the **nacreous layer**. This pearly layer is laid down by the mantle throughout the life of the clam. It is made up of calcium carbonate crystals which are laid down parallel to the mantle surface. This is the same substance of which **pearls** are made by the mantle.

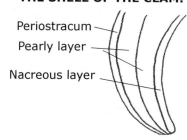

CROSS-SECTION OF THE SHELL OF THE CLAM:

Periostracum

Pearly layer

Nacreous layer

3. The **hinge** of the clam is the place where the valves connect and articulate. There is a black fibrous **hinge ligament** which keeps the valves attached to each other. On the inside of the clam, you will see teeth in the shell which articulate with the other shell. These strengthen the alignment of the two shells.

Interior structure:

1. Holding your clam securely, slip the knife into the space between the shells near the position of the adductor muscles. If you have difficulty finding a place to insert the knife, scrape the edge of the clam in order to break off some of the tips of the shells. This should reveal a crack between the valves. Now, slip your knife into the crack and carefully cut the adductor muscles on either side of the clam. Do not just run your knife into the clam or you will damage some of the internal organs. You must cut the muscles on each side of the clam in order to open it.

2. Once the clam's muscles are cut, you will be able to open it, but be very careful so that you do not tear the internal organs apart as you open the shells. The mantle may tear a little, but just carefully separate it from one of the shells.

3. The covering of the organs is called the **mantle** and it separates the **shell** from the organs. The mantle protects against abrasion. Within the mantle, you will observe a massive **foot**. This is the structure some species of clam use for burrowing. It can extend outside of the shells and holds the intestine. This double function is an example of the compactness of the design of the clam. The mantle produces the shell by excreting **calcium carbonate**.

4. The clam is a filter feeder. In other words, it strains food particles out of the water. So, as the organism pulls water into the shells for its oxygen supply it is also feeding. An **incurrent siphon** pulls water in. The water flows past the **gills** which look like feathery or leafy ridges. The oxygen is exchanged and the water proceeds to the labial palps which separate the food particles from inedible matter. The water then continues around to the **excurrent siphon**. Near this is the **excretory organ** which discards poisons from the blood and the **anus** which discards indigestible matter. The water, laden with these by-products and waste materials, leaves through the excurrent siphon.

INTERIOR STRUCTURE OF THE CLAM: WITH CUTAWAY OF THE FOOT SHOWING THE INTESTINE AND GONAD.

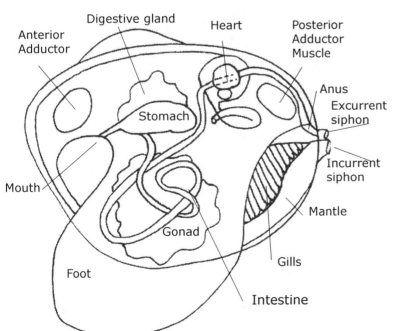

HEART OF THE CLAM: SHOWS OPEN SYSTEM

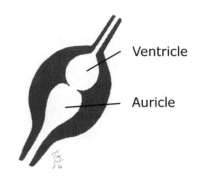

Ventricle

Auricle

5. The circulatory system of the clam is open, that is, the blood does not stay in the blood vessels. The pumping action for the blood is performed by a straight-line chambered **heart** which rhythmically forces the blood through the system. The blood leaves the vessels and is forced through **sinuses** to circulate the nutrients and gasses needed by the clam.

6. The digestive system is interesting in its design. The food is propelled through the gills towards the **mouth** by **cilia** on the gill arches. The mouth leads to the stomach where the food particles are ground by the **style** with a mortar and pestle type of action. The style is a slender, crystalline cone. The material of which it is made is a digestive enzyme. As the style rotates to help grind the food it grinds bits of itself, the digestive enzyme, into the food. The food then passes into the intestine where it is absorbed. To expose the intestine, carefully cut a flap out of the foot like that indicated by the dotted line in the drawing. Digestive juices are provided by the **digestive gland** which surrounds the stomach. Undigested material passes out of the **anus** which can be found near the excurrent siphon.

GILL OF THE CLAM: SHOWS CILIATED MEANS OF PROPELLING FOOD

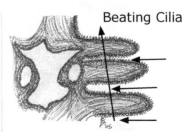

Beating Cilia

Arrows show path of food particles

7. You can cut a small portion (about 1 cm²) of a gill section and mount it on a depression slide with a cover slip. This will show you the **gill cilia**. If your specimen is poorly preserved, they may be difficult to see.

8. The clams reproduce bisexually when the adults release sperm and eggs into the water. Within a few hours of fertilization, the cell has become a free swimming larval form which looks nothing like the future adult. The clam is designed to allow its progeny to survive environmental shocks. If a temperature change is rapid, or if a chemical is released into the waters where clams live, they may spontaneously release sperm and eggs. Thus, the free swimming larvae may be able to escape the stressor.

9. Look for the **adductor muscle**. Scrape it with your knife so that you remove the muscle down to the shell. You should be able to see a mark where the muscle was attached. This is the **muscle scar**. When a mollusk is fossilized, the carbonate shell is normally the only thing preserved. In the shell, the investigator can see the scars of the muscle attachments. Then, the strength of the clam to stay closed can be determined. A smaller muscle should be near the adductor. This is the **foot retractor muscle** which pulls back the foot. It does not need to be very large since the foot comes in easily when the adductor contracts. The adductor together with the shell is the chief defense for the clam. Starfishes love to eat clams (like some humans) and they open the shells by attaching to both of the shells and pulling outward against the strength of the adductors. Eventually, one or the other organism tires and the battle ends. (Ad is Latin for 'to'. Ab is Latin for 'away from'.)

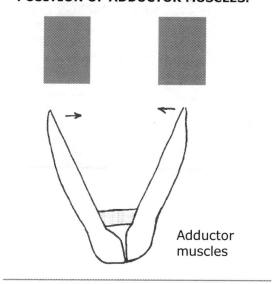

SIDE VIEW OF CLAM: SHOWING THE POSITION OF ADDUCTOR MUSCLES.

Adductor muscles

INTERIOR VIEW OF THE CLAM SHOWING THE SHELL ONLY.

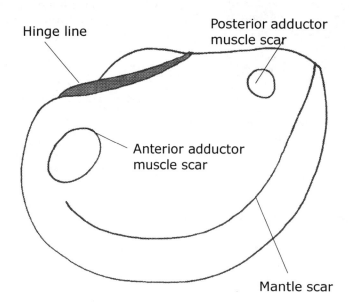

Hinge line

Posterior adductor muscle scar

Anterior adductor muscle scar

Mantle scar

DISSECTION: CLAM

Name: _____

Date: _____

Critical Thinking:

1. Why do you think that the presence of an adductor muscle would leave a scar? Hint: What organ produces the interior pearly layer of the clam?

_____

_____

_____

2. How are pearls formed? How are cultured pearls formed? What makes the pearls round?

_____

_____

_____

3. Test the pH of sea water if some is available. Why would acid resistance be an advantage to the clam? Try this: Drop vinegar (or HCL, hydrochloric acid) on the outer part of the shell of your clam. Then try it on the inner part. Is there a difference in resistance between the two parts?

_____

_____

_____

4. The clam is used as an indicator of levels of pollution in water. Explain why we need indicators of pollution and why the clam might be a good one. *Note: Clams like clear water as well as clean water. Look up the action of the gill cilia. This is very sensitive to chemical input.*

_____

_____

_____

5. The foot of the clam also holds the intestine. Why is this a good design for a mollusk? Can you list another example of double function in the clam? Describe both of these functions and how thay fit together.

_____

_____

_____

6. If you found a clam fossil on a mountain, what could you hypothesize about the environment in which it was alive? *Hint: What was necessary for that clam to live? It would be a fair assumption to make that the requirements for clams were the same or very close to the requirements for clams now.*

_____

_____

_____

_____

CLAM

Name:_____

Date:_____

Phylum_____

Class _____

Order_____

Family _____

Genus _____

species _____

Scientific Name _____

Common Name _____

EXTERNAL

INTERNAL

12 | Dissection: Earthworm

MATERIALS

Earthworm   Dissection Pan
Dissection Kit

The earthworm is a really interesting organism. It is designed to move through the upper layers of the soil eating very tiny organisms and pieces of organic matter. The fecal material of the earthworm has long been known to add to the fertility of the soil. Chemical fertilizers and insecticides kill off the earthworms and thus reduce the life sustaining nature of the soil. This is one of the trade-offs we must make as we artificially increase our land's productivity.

One of the things which make the earthworm unique is its structure. The segmented worms are called so because their bodies are divided externally into distinct segments. Internally, certain organs are also reproduced in each segment. Not all of the segments are identical, but there is a lot of similarity of design between the segments.

External structure:

1. The worm has **segments** running down its body. These are counted starting with the anterior end. In the first segment is the **prostomium**. The **mouth** is directly under this.

2. Around segments 31 to 37 is the **clitellum**, a lighter-colored band of tissue surrounding the worm segments which perform roles in the reproduction of the earthworm.

3. Along the ventral side of the worm are pairs of **setae**, thickened hair-like bristles which help the worm move through the ground. More difficult to

see are the **nephridiopores**, the excretory outlets on the lateral ventral side of each segment. Urea and ammonia are excreted at these sites.

4. The **anus** is at the extreme posterior of the organism.

Internal structure:

1. Rest the worm on the ventral side. Carefully, with a sharp scalpel, draw a thin cut down the dorsal side. ***Do not cut too deeply.*** As you cut down the length of the organism, you will have to pull the skin outward away from the organs and pin it so that it will stay out. As you try to do this you will have to cut through the septa which separate the segments. Continue in this way the length of the worm. As you open the earthworm you will notice that the internal structure of each segment is not the same as all the others although it looks that way externally.

EARTHWORM INTESTINE CROSS-SECTION SHOWING TYPHLOSOLE.

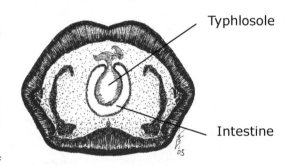

Typhlosole

Intestine

2. Even though the worm has very few large organs, it is not a simple organism. All of the functions necessary for life are handled by this worm. You will find no lungs or gills, though the worm breathes air. Perhaps you have noticed that the earthworms come to the surface of the ground during a heavy rain. They exchange gases through the outer **epidermal layer,** their skin. There is a system of capillaries within the skin and oxygen is absorbed into the tissues of the skin. The worms cannot get enough air when water fills the spaces between the soil particles.

Hemoglobin carries oxygen absorbed through the skin to other parts of the body. Half of the oxygen needs of the worm are met through the use of hemoglobin in the blood. The other half is met through direct absorption.

ANTERIOR NERVOUS SYSTEM OF THE EARTHWORM.

This is a very complex network. Notice how tightly the prostomium is enervated. (After Barnes after Hess from Avel.)

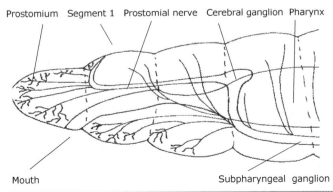

Prostomium   Segment 1   Prostomial nerve   Cerebral ganglion   Pharynx

Mouth   Subpharyngeal ganglion

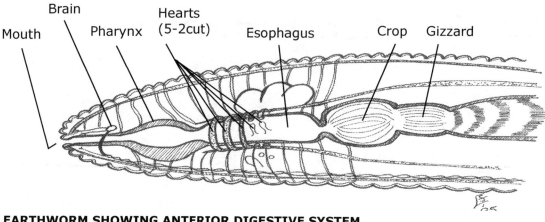

EARTHWORM SHOWING ANTERIOR DIGESTIVE SYSTEM

3. The earthworm is well known for its helpful fertilization of the soil. The worms take soil in by **mouth** and use the organics within the soil for food. Some minerals are absorbed from the soil, also. (like calcium) From the mouth the food passes into the **pharynx** (segment 5), the **esophagus** (segments 6- 14) , the **crop** (segments 15-16), the **gizzard** (segment 20), and the **intestine** (the rest of the worm). The intestine is the location of the absorption of digested nutrients. In order to facilitate this action the surface area of the intestinal wall has been increased by a fold in the upper wall of the intestine. This fold hangs down into the intestine. This fold is called the **typhlosole**. Undigested matter as well as some calcium secreted into the intestine pass out of the worm through the **anus**.

4. Running just under the skin on the ventral side (opposite where you cut lengthwise down the worm) is the **ventral blood vessel**. The **dorsal blood vessel** will lie above the intestine. You probably cut into it in several places, but you should be able to find it. These vessels are connected by transverse vessels which are smaller and more difficult to see. The **hearts** of the earthworm are in the segments 7 - 11. These connect the dorsal and ventral vessels and pump the blood through the **closed circulatory system**. These hearts contract to force the movement of the blood. The dorsal blood vessel is contractile and provides most of the force to pump the blood. It has one-way valves which force the blood to flow only one direction.

5. There are **ganglia** which you may be able to find. The earthworm has a nervous system which allows the worm to sense environmental hazards and other worms. In Segment 2, there is an enlarged ganglion which is the **brain**. This will be found dorsal to the pharynx. Ventral to the pharynx is the first **segmental ganglion**. The segmental ganglia will look like little swellings on the ventral surface under the pharynx. The **prostomium** is at the very front of the earthworm and is well enervated. It is directly connected to the brain which is immediately behind it.

DIGESTIVE SYSTEM OF AN EARTHWORM: DORSAL VIEW

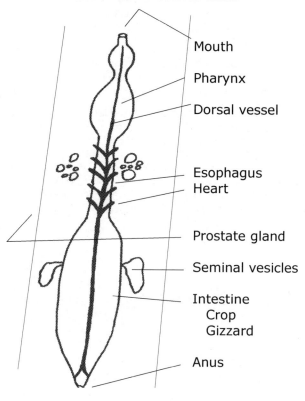

DISSECTION: EARTHWORM

Name:_____

Date:_____

Critical Thinking:

1. Why does the worm need its blood in a closed system? A closed system means that the blood is forcibly pushed around to all the organs in a certain order to re-oxygenate them and to remove their wastes. Why do you hypothesize that this is necessary in the earthworm? Hint: Observe how the worm moves. Where would such a fluid in an open system end up?

_____

_____

_____

2. Since the worm uses hemoglobin in the blood, what would you guess about the color of its blood?

_____

_____

3. The setae are important in what way? How are they used?

_____

_____

4. Describe the method of locomotion of the earthworm.

_____

Where would the worm's muscles used to do this be located?

_____

Are they there? (Look at your worm.)

_____

How are they oriented?

_____

In what direction is their motion?

_____

5. The placement of the anus is efficient. Why? (Name at least two reasons.)

1. _____

2. _____

6. Most life forms are segmented in some way, that is, their parts are divided into sections. The earthworm is segmented in an unusual degree of repetition. Hypothesize as to the usefulness of segmentation. How might this characteristic be helpful or unhelpful?

_____

_____

_____

EARTHWORM

Name:_____
Date:_____

Phylum_____

Class _____

Order_____

Family _____

Genus _____

species _____

Scientific Name _____

Common Name _____

EXTERNAL

INTERNAL

13 | Dissection: Grasshopper

MATERIALS

Grasshopper   Dissection Pan
Dissection Kit

The phylum Arthropoda, or jointed legs, is a very populous group. This laboratory manual will have dissection instructions for one of them, the grasshopper, a member of class insecta, but the crayfish (or crawfish), a member of class crustacea is also a common example of arthropoda. The grasshopper and the crayfish have many parts in common especially the basic structure of the appendages.

Crickets, locusts, grasshoppers, and roaches all belong to the same order, Orthoptera (Or-*thop*-ter-a). These organisms have biting mouth parts. This is a fairly appropriate observation considering the all-devouring reputation of locusts. Their forewings are leathery and the hind wings are membranous. They are herbivorous.

External Structure:

1. The grasshopper has three main body parts: **head, thorax, and abdomen.** The head should be observed under magnification for best viewing. Make side and front view drawings of this part. The **compound** eyes are prominent and are on either side of the head. Between them in a triangular arrangement, are the three **ocelli** (singular: **ocellus**). Towards the mouth and in line with the ocelli are the **antennae** (usually pronounced an-ten-y) (singular: antenna).

2. The mouth parts are rather more complicated. It is best to think of them as grinding and cutting plates. Some of them are very sharp and others are used to control the food as it is cut up. Find and draw these parts: **Labrum, Mandibles, Maxillae, Labium**. The maxillae has several parts, as does the Labium.

3. The thorax is made up of three sections. The **Prothorax** has the first set of legs attached. Please note that in spite of all these strange, new names, the names of the leg parts are familiar: **femur, tibia, tarsus, and claws.** The **Mesothorax** has the second set of legs and the **forewings** (leathery). It also has a pair of **spiracles** located one on each side just behind the articulation with the prothorax. The last segment, or **metathorax**, has the third set of legs and the second pair of wings, the **hind wings** (membranous). There is a pair of spiracles, also.

4. The **abdomen** of the grasshopper is also segmented. There are eleven segments each of the first eight with a set of **spiracles** on either side. There are no legs on the abdomen. The **anus** is at the end of the body, as are the **external genital organs**. On each segment are a pair of appendages. On the eighth and ninth segments on females, the appendages are ovipositors. These help deposit the eggs. In the male, the ninth segment's appendages are copulatory organs. In bees and other Hymenoptera, the eighth and ninth appendages are stingers, saws and piercers.

The spiracles are controlled by muscles which open or close the spiracles. The first four work together to inhale while the last six remain closed, then the first four close and the last six open and exhale. These are the external openings of the grasshopper respiratory system. There is a system of canals and air sacs within the body of the insects which fills and empties with air as the insect moves around. This is also the secret as to why roaches and other orthoptera can survive so long under water. The air sacs store gases quite well, delaying the need for constant air sources.

Have you not understood since the earth was founded? He sits enthroned above the circle of the earth, and its people are like grasshoppers.
Isaiah 40:21-22

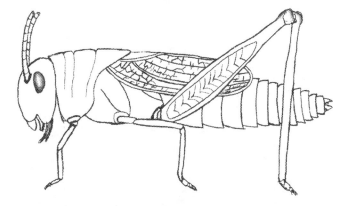

GRASSHOPPER: CROSS-SECTION

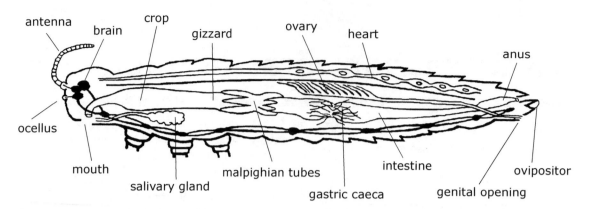

Internal Structures:

1. The grasshopper may be opened either ventrally or dorsally. Either way you will probably damage some of the organs on the initial incision. This description will be from the ventral entry. Carefully, remove the legs, looking them over and drawings them. With the grasshopper on its back, take a sharp scalpel and cut lengthwise down the body from the mouth parts to the anus.

2. Carefully, pull the sides apart and pin them down. The exoskeleton is rigid, so bend it in such a way that the tender organs within are not destroyed. a short esophagus leads from the **mouth** to the **crop** and on to the **gizzard**. At the junction of the gizzard and the stomach you will see the **gastric caeca**, short extensions of the digestive system which the digestion process. At the junction of the stomach and the intestine you will find the **malpighian tubes,** These are thin tubes which perform the function of kidneys for the grasshopper. They excrete wastes into the intestine to get rid of the poisons from the body. From the intestine the food travels to the **rectum** where it is expelled from the body through the **anus**.

3. Lying on the ventral side of the gizzard you should see the **salivary glands**. The **ventral nerve cord** stretches the length of the ventral side just under the exoskeleton. It extends forward to larger ganglion next to the esophagus. There the ventral nerve cord splits in two and runs around the esophagus, meeting again at the **ganglia** behind the eyes of the grasshopper. The **brain** is an enlarged ganglion just dorsal and slightly posterior to the optical ganglia.

4. The genital system lies in the abdomen dorsal to the intestine. Carefully lift the intestine and stomach aside. under them will lie the female's **ovary**. It is connected to the outside, at the **genital opening**.

5. Under the ovary is the **pericardial membrane** which separates the **heart** and **aorta** from the abdominal cavity.

A LEG OF THE GRASSHOPPER.

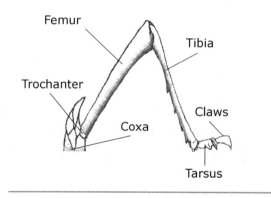

THE THORAX AND ASSOCIATED LEGS

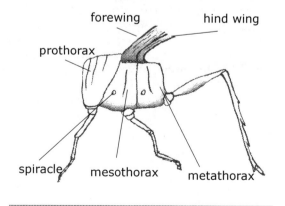

DISSECTION: GRASSHOPPER

Name:_____
Date:_____

Critical Thinking:

1. Did you see any evidence of a skeletal system in your grasshopper?

_____

What part of the insect serves the support function for the grasshopper?

_____

_____

2. What about a muscular system? Do you notice one?

_____

_____

How does the grasshopper move its legs?

_____

_____

3. The mouth parts of the grasshopper have been studied by many students down through the years. What type of motion does the grasshopper use to tear or cut its food?

_____

_____

Does the insect use any legs to support the food while it is chewing?

_____

_____

4. Look at the legs. Are there any of them which appear to be designed for jumping? Which ones?

_____

_____

EXTERNAL PARTS OF THE GRASSHOPPER

GRASSHOPPER

Name:_____
Date:_____

Phylum_____

Class _____

Order _____

Family _____

Genus _____

species _____

Scientific Name _____

Common Name _____

14 | Dissection: Fish

MATERIALS

Fish   Dissection Pan
Dissection Kit

The external features of the fish reveal an aquatic creature designed for speed and stability in the water. Observe the direction of the overlap of scales and the smooth texture of their layering. The aerodynamic streamlining of the fish and the placement of the stabilizing fins make it fast and agile in the water. The method of breathing, in through the mouth and out through the gill slits, is also a streamlining asset. All these things and others show a creature which is obviously designed for locomotion and life in general under the water.

External Features:

1. Take your fish and lay it in the pan, dorsal side away from you. Make a drawing of the fish in this position, labeling the **fins, spines, rays, lateral line**, and the other items found in the box.

Dorsal fin	Rays
(anterior & posterior)	Nostrils
Pectoral fins	Maxilla
Anal fin	Mandible
Caudal fin	Operculum
Dorsal fin	Anus
Pelvic fin	Eye
Lateral line	Gills
Spines	Scales

2. Next, pick up the fish and turn it so that it faces you. Draw the outline of this view of the fish. Try to make it to the same scale as the side view.

3. Spread the fins to their fullest extent and draw them. Observe their structure and whether they are supported by the stiff spines, the more flexible rays, or a combination of both. Fill in the box on fins.

4. Remove several scales, rinse in water and observe as a wet mount under the microscope. Notice the concentric circles. The scales increase in size during the life of the fish, instead of increasing in number. How many are there on a scale from your fish? Are there any differences in structure between the portion which was embedded and the part which overlapped the next scale? Make a drawing of the scale.

5. Open the mouth. Make a written description of the interior, including the shape and function of the teeth. How is the tongue attached and where? Where are the nostrils and what is their use. If you insert a probe into a nostril does it enter the mouth cavity? From the mouth cavity can you see out of the operculum covering the gills?

Name of Fin	Number of Fins	Location	Function	How Supported (ray or spine)
Pectoral				
Dorsal				
Anal				
Pelvic				
Caudal				

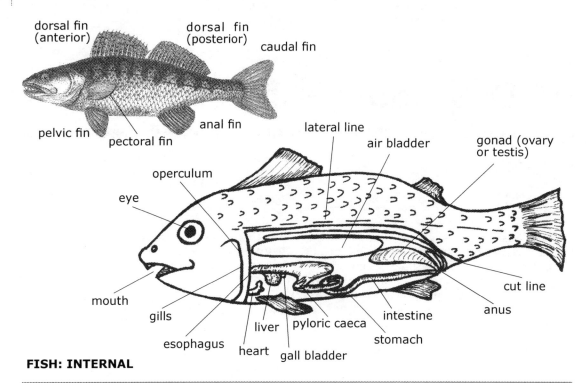

FISH: INTERNAL

Internal construction:

1. Holding the fish anterior side away from you, insert your scissors just anterior to the anus. Cut upwards anteriorly along the line between the anus and the mouth. Then, lay the fish down and continue the cut towards the dorsal side, until you come to the end of the body cavity. Now, cut from your starting point parallel to your second cut towards the dorsal side until you run out of body cavity. Now, carefully cut across the body cavity next to the spine and the top of the body cavity. The body cavity should be completely exposed. If not, cut away any leftover flaps of material.

2. Make your first drawing showing the exposed body cavity and organs. The **liver** is in the anterior end of the body cavity. Lift it up and you should be able to see the gall bladder. Removing the liver will expose the **stomach** and its attached **esophagus**. The **pyloric caeca**, or pouches, are located at the junction of the stomach and the intestine.

3. Cut the digestive tract at the esophagus and anus and remove it. Label all the parts in your drawing.

4. In the female, the **gonads** will be a yellow ovary containing many eggs causing it to be large. In the male, the **testes** are in the same place as the **ovary** in the female, but smaller and creamy-white, not yellow.

The urogenital opening is the external outlet for the urinary bladder. The ducts connecting the bladder with the gonads are very thin and may be difficult to see.

5. The air bladder is at the top of the body cavity. The dark **kidneys** will be dorsal to the **air bladder** up against the spine.

6. The pericardial cavity which holds the heart, lies in the isthmus, the narrow area between the mouth and the main part of the body. Carefully cut into the pericardial cavity and expose the heart. Locate the parts of the **heart**: **Cardinal vein, atrium, sinus venosus, bulbus arteriosus, ventricle, ventral aorta**.

7. Remove a **gill arch**. Observe with a magnifying lens. Can you see the **gill filaments** and the **gill rakers**?

FISH: HEART

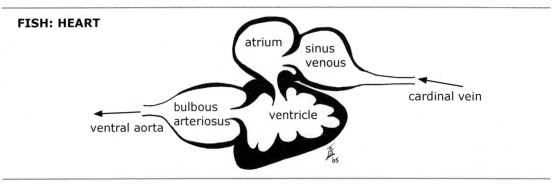

DISSECTION: FISH

Name:_____

Date:_____

Critical Thinking:

1. How old is your fish (approximately)? Why is the scale of a fish a reasonably good indicator of the age of the fish? Explain how the seasons affect the fish scale.

_____

_____

_____

_____

_____

EXTERNAL

2. How does the fish breathe? Whence comes its oxygen? Are there any similarities of function between gills and lungs?

_____

_____

_____

_____

3. Suggest a use the fish might have for the spines in the dorsal fin.

_____

_____

_____

Name of Fin	Number of Fins	Location	Function	How Supported (ray or spine)
Pectoral				
Dorsal				
Anal				
Pelvic				
Caudal				

4. What does the structure of the fish's tooth tell you about the diet of the fish?

_____

_____

5. If the water is carried through the mouth to the gills, of what use to the fish are the nostrils?

_____

_____

6. The air bladder is a special organ for the fish. What function does it perform?

_____

_____

Why do you think that the location up close to the spine and the top of the body cavity is helpful to the fish?

_____

_____

7. How many gill arches did you observe on each side of the fish?

_____

_____

What function could the gill rakers perform for the fish?

_____

_____

Why would the gill covers aid the fish while swimming?

_____

_____

8. Why do the fins face to the posterior of the fish?

_____

_____

_____

Look at the front face of the fish.
Draw the front view.

What can you observe about its shape?

_____

_____

FISH

Name:_____
Date:_____

Phylum _____

Class _____

Order _____

Family _____

Genus _____

species _____

Scientific Name _____

Common Name _____

15 | Dissection: Fetal Pig

MATERIALS

Dissection Kit	Fetal Pig: preserved
Dissection Pan	Long Pins

The dissection of a fetal pig is good experience for the high school student for at least two reasons: the pig is large enough for the relatively inexperienced student to easily dissect and the anatomy of the pig is fairly similar to larger mammalian forms, like us.

Students nearly always ask where the fetal pigs come from. The pigs are taken from the slaughtered mother pigs, preserved and injected for use by students. As a pregnant sow weighs more, it is not uncommon for sows to be slaughtered when pregnant.

The thin layer of cells on the outside of the pig is called the epitrichum and would have been sloughed off as the hair grew. You can wash this off, but do it outside with a brush, as the epitrichum will clog drains.

External Features:

Pinna: external ear, fleshy, used to focus sound waves.

Eyes: have upper and lower fleshy eyelids.

Nictitating membrane: at the nasal corner of the eye. It is used to moisten and clean the eye. The corners of the eyelids may need to be slit in order to see this membrane.

Nares: external openings to the nose.

Vibrissae: Protruding hairs from a fleshy lump under the chin.

Forelimb: Find **wrist, forearm, elbow, upper arm, shoulder**.

Hind limb: Find the **ankle, calf, knee, thigh**, and **hip**.

Ventral surface: You will note the **umbilical cord** and mammary papilla on both sexes. In the male, the **urogenital opening** is posterior to the umbilical cord. The **penis** extends posteriorly just under the skin, and the **scrotum** is just ventral to the anus which is under the tail. In the female, the **urogenital opening** is under the **anus** which is just ventral to the tail. In both sexes the urinary waste disposal system shares an opening with the genital system.

The umbilical cord has four tubes within it: two **umbilical arteries**, an **umbilical vein**, and the **allantoic stalk.** The umbilical arteries transport blood and carbon dioxide to the placenta. The umbilical vein returns maternal nutrients to the fetus, and the allantoic stalk allows urine to pass from the bladder to the amnionic sac.

Oral cavity: Cut the hinge point of the jaws and open the mouth wide for examination. Observe the different types of teeth present. The pig is an omnivore and needs teeth with which to handle different types of food and chewing.

Tongue: A muscular organ used to move and swallow food. Also possesses sensory buds on the edges of the tongue.

Epiglottis: A flap of tissue extending from the base of the tongue into a hole in the roof of the throat. This prevents food from entering the trachea.

FETAL PIG: EXTERNAL FEATURES.

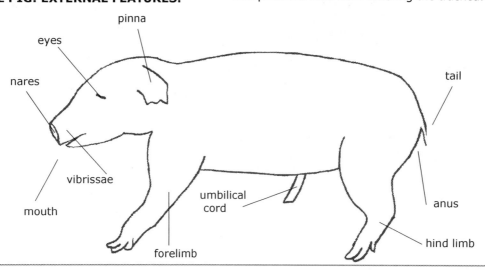

Internal Structure:

Place the pig in the tray ventral side up and run a string from one forelimb under the tray and to the other forelimb. Tie the string to the forelimb tight enough to pull the limbs apart. Do the same with the hind limbs.

Observe the cut lines in the drawing. When you cut into the pig, remember that the first cut is always a little awkward. Be careful not to cut too deep before you can see what is underneath the skin.

Use the scissors for the opening of the thoracic wall. Some books will recommend using the scalpel, but resist this since cutting through the skin only dulls your blade for the more delicate work later on. While you are cutting through the skin, pull the scissors upwards in order to keep the points from poking into the organs below.

Make your cuts around the umbilical cord and down the sides of the abdomen. Cut all the way to the tray and pin the skin with your long pins slanted out from the pig. You will notice that the skin is not loose around the organs but is attached by means of membranes and thin ligaments. Gently trim these with your scalpel as you pull the skin away and down to be pinned. There will be a blood vessel going from the umbilicus into the liver. Tie a thin string around to identify this umbilical vein later. Cut the umbilical vein under the umbilicus where it extends down into the internal organs. Lay the cord and surrounding skin down between the legs and out of the way.

Make your cuts in the order specified in the drawing. If it seems easier to make your cuts out of order, no problem. The important things to remember at this stage are: do not damage the underlying organs and try to keep the skin in large pieces to make it easier to keep out of the way with pins.

FETAL PIG SHOWING CUT LINES FOR DISSECTION

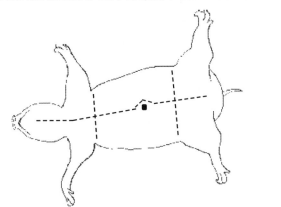

As you cut over the thoracic cavity, you will have to be careful to keep the tips of the scissors up so as not to damage the heart. You must cut through the ribs and the sternum in order to

open the cavity. The cut under the forelimbs will be through fatty tissue and not only skin, so it will be a thicker cut. You will have to pull the ribs apart in order to open the thoracic cavity. They may be difficult to pin down unless you crack the ribs, so expect some resistance to opening.

After you have made your cuts, rinse the body cavity out and throw away the pieces of latex, skin, etc. which are cluttering up your dissection. At this point you should have a nice, clean exposed body cavity. There may be some remaining connective tissue between the organs which you can clear away now.

The thoracic and abdominal cavities are separated by a thin muscular wall, the **diaphragm,** which is cupped over the liver. Trim the diaphragm away from the flaps of skin you are pulling away from the body to be pinned down. Do not cut the diaphragm out, but leave it in position.

FETAL PIG THROAT

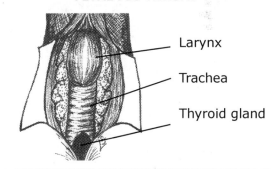

Larynx

Trachea

Thyroid gland

Carefully open the ventral part of the neck exposing the large, firm **larynx**, the voice box. On the sides of the larynx is a large soft mass of tissue, called the **thymus**. This organ produces the T-cells which attack foreign particles in the system. This organ is most large in the fetus and infant, getting smaller as the animal ages and develops. The thymus extends down to the heart in the fetal pig. Just posterior to the larynx, between the thymus glands is the **thyroid gland.** It is generally darker than the thymus.

The thyroid lies upon the **trachea** (actually, it is dorsal to the thyroid). Note the cartilaginous rings surrounding the trachea. These add support to the structure while still maintaining flexibility. Your vacuum cleaner hose probably uses the same idea for the same reasons. When the trachea is bent, the passageway will stay open because of these rings. Gently, lift the trachea and observe the tube just dorsal to it, the **esophagus**. The esophagus is the pipe by which food and drink enters the digestive tract.

Carefully, clean away the mesentery which connects the diaphragm to the organs within the thoracic cavity. On the anterior side of the diaphragm, is a tube going through the diaphragm. This is the esophagus leading down to the stomach.

On the other side of the diaphragm is the **abdominal cavity**. The large liver is posterior to the diaphragm and the stomach is dorsal to the liver. The stomach appears to be sac-like, especially in the fetal pig since it has not been used yet to hold solid food.

FETAL PIG: DIGESTIVE SYSTEM

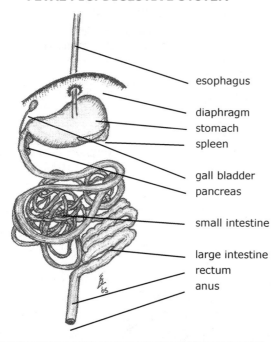

- esophagus
- diaphragm
- stomach
- spleen
- gall bladder
- pancreas
- small intestine
- large intestine
- rectum
- anus

At the end of the esophagus where it connects with the stomach, you will find the cardiac sphincter. This is a circular lump of muscle you should be able to feel with your fingers. This valve keeps the food in the stomach from passing back up into the esophagus again.

Lift the lobe of the liver with the string attached. Underneath and embedded in the lobe will be the gall bladder, in which is stored bile for digestion.

At the posterior end of the stomach (on the pig's right side) you can feel the pyloric sphincter which keeps the food in the stomach until digestion has proceeded to a certain point. The small intestine takes the food over to the pig's left side past the pancreas which lies within the mesentery which supports the small intestine. The pancreas extends over towards the left side of the pig next to the spleen. The pancreas regulates the amount of sugar in the blood stream and excretes digestive juices into the small intestine. The spleen does not provide a digestive function but acts as a reservoir for the blood, capable of injecting an additional 500 cc into the blood stream.

The small intestine empties into the large intestine. The main differences between the two in the pig are, of course, the diameter size and the increased mesenteric binding of the large intestine. It moves as a unit within the abdominal cavity. Within the large intestine, water and mineral nutrients are absorbed. Also absorbed are vitamins produced by the action of beneficial bacteria present in the caecum, a small sac-like organ at the junction of the small intestine and the large intestine. The ilio-colic sphincter separates the two intestines and prevents the digesting material from going up the digestive system. The large intestine ends at the rectum which stores the waste materials, the undigestable or undigested foods until they are expelled through the anus.

There are other organs in this area of the pig. They are parts of the urogenital system. The maintenance of an organism is dependent upon the organism's ability to maintain chemical balances within the body. This equilibrium is called homeostasis, a state of sameness. The kidneys lie dorsal to the intestines, one on either side of the spine. They have a protective membrane around them. From within the concave side of the kidney passes the ureter, a tube which propels the urine and its associated waste products to the urinary bladder. These wastes have been filtered out of the blood stream and are not associated with the digestive process. The urine is stored in the bladder until it is expelled from the body. In the fetal pig, the kidneys are functioning and the urine passes out into the amniotic fluid in which the fetal pig floats. Remove one of the kidneys and slice it open carefully. Attempt to identify the **ureter**, the **renal cortex**, the **renal medulla**, and the **renal pelvis**. These are all similar to that of the human kidney.

KIDNEYS AND ASSOCIATED STRUCTURES

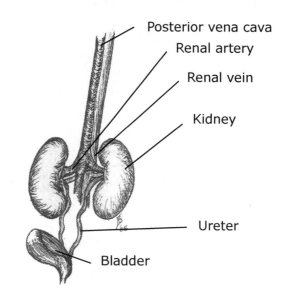

- Posterior vena cava
- Renal artery
- Renal vein
- Kidney
- Ureter
- Bladder

FETAL PIG: REPRODUCTIVE SYSTEMS

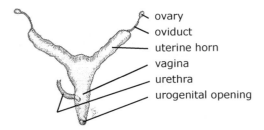

- ovary
- oviduct
- uterine horn
- vagina
- urethra
- urogenital opening

Female system

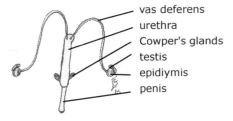

- vas deferens
- urethra
- Cowper's glands
- testis
- epidiymis
- penis

Male system

If your pig is female, the **ovaries** may be found posterior to the kidneys. They will be two small yellow masses of tissue. They are as yet undeveloped in the fetal pig. The ovaries are connected to the uterine horn by the oviducts. The egg will be propelled through the **oviducts** to the **uterine horns**. Once there the eggs, if fertilized, implant and grow. In the pig the shape of the uterine environment is branched and fetal pigs develop along the two branches. At the approach of birth, the piglets will pass through the vagina. The urethra also connects to this structure, allowing urine to be expelled through the same opening. This is why the system is called the urogenital system, because of the dual uses of the organs.

In the male, the **penis** is the outlet for urine from the **urinary bladder** as well as for the sperm necessary to fertilize eggs to produce young. The sperm are produced in the **testes** which will be located in the scrotum if the pig is greater than 20 cm long. (Assuming that the size of the fetal pig is directly related to the age of the pig.) If the pig is less than 20 cm., the testes may be visible within the abdominal cavity, as two firm organs. The descent of the testes into the scrotum allows the sperm to escape the high body temperatures present in the abdominal cavity.

The respiratory system can be observed in the thoracic cavity. The trachea has been seen already. Carefully trace the bronchial tubes to the lungs. Note the branching of the tubing. The name: bronchial tube is derived from this similarity to trees. Carefully cut one of the lungs out and open it up. What can you observe about the lung tissue?

The heart has a tough membrane surrounding it which has some fluid within. The membrane is the pericardium, which serves the heart to lubricate it reducing friction with the surrounding organs.

Note the placement of the heart within the thoracic cavity and observe the arteries and veins which leave and enter the heart. Make your drawing of this before you go on. The heart should be removed to study the four chambers and to draw them.

FETAL PIG: MAJOR ORGANS

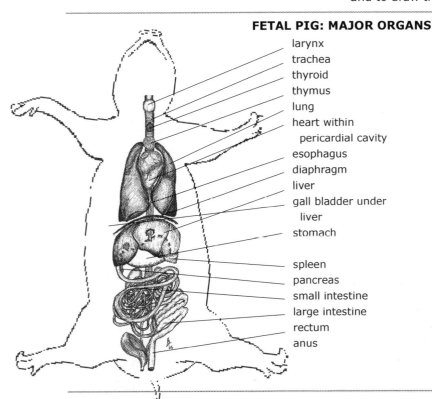

- larynx
- trachea
- thyroid
- thymus
- lung
- heart within
   pericardial cavity
- esophagus
- diaphragm
- liver
- gall bladder under
   liver
- stomach
- spleen
- pancreas
- small intestine
- large intestine
- rectum
- anus

While you finish up this dissection, always remember that there are reasons which determine the placement of an organ, or its structure. The questions you must ask nearly always begin with the word, why.

Also, remember that your pig may not match the drawing in this laboratory manual or in any other because pigs like humans are all different.

DISSECTION: FETAL PIG

Name:_____

Date:_____

Critical Thinking:

1. If your pig has been injected, trace the arteries and make a drawing showing them. Where are the vessels going from the heart which have not been oxygenated yet?

2. If the kidney were to fail to work correctly what would be the effect upon the organism? What does the kidney dialysis machine do and how often must the machine be used by the patient?

_____

_____

_____

_____

_____

3. The human fetus carries a good supply of red blood cells, so many that the body usually breaks down a few after the baby has been born. If the red blood cells carry the oxygen around the body. what purpose would you hypothesize for the extra supply of red blood cells for the baby while unborn?

_____

_____

_____

_____

_____

4. If you have a pair of mail cutters, you can open the brain case and check out the pig's brain. Make a drawing showing the main parts of it. What useful purpose can you see for the division between the thinking portion of the brain and the automatic portion?

_____

_____

_____

_____

_____

FETAL PIG

Name: _____

Date: _____

Phylum _____

Class _____

Order _____

Family _____

Genus _____

species _____

Scientific Name _____

Common Name _____

16 | Classification of Animals I

The classification of animals began traditionally with the naturalist, Linnaeus, who was systematic about the naming of animals, grouping them according to their structure. Most classification today is still done by methods based on the structure of the animal, although at times the scientist must go to very minute differences to separate the types.

Because of the benefits of using a classification system, scientists spend a great deal of time on the systems that they use. However, it must be emphasized that any classification system is not perfect; a system only groups organisms so that they can be studied more easily. A classification system is not a statement of some relationship between animals, except of that relationship which speaks of like structure. So, animals may be placed into another group if a consensus of scientists agrees that the organism is more similar to the second group. The student should remember that the structures may not occur in sets, but may be mixed causing confusion about the classification. An example for this occurs with the platypus. And, this is not an isolated example. So, remember that a system of classification: can be challenged, can change, does not indicate relationships except in form, and only describes nature; it cannot dictate nature.

The grouping of structures in classification systems is primarily by function. For example, the first function is that of support. A classifier will attempt to determine the mechanism used for support for a particular organism. There are several ways in which an organism can be supported: through internal methods and external methods.

Internal methods can include: membranes controlling osmotic pressure, semi-hard articulated skeletal systems, hard articulated skeletal systems, both semi-hard and hard unarticulated skeletons. Each of these methods has been used to separate animals into groups.

The exercise for this topic is really a demonstration of the usefulness and the limitations of an artificial classification system.

Procedure I:

1. Observe the drawings on the next page. Classify them according to their type of appendages. In your classifications, make sure that no shapes are left unclassified.

2. Reclassify them according to their shape.

3. Classify them again, but this time use your own system. You make up the rules of classification. Do not break your own rules of classification.

4. In each of the previous classifications, count the numbers in each set. Calculate the percentage of each type as compared to the whole group. For example, there may be 45% with appendages.

5. Count the number of drawings which would fit into two or more of the sets. What is their percentage of the whole? What is the percentage of drawings which do not fit into any group?

Now the Lord God had formed out of the ground all the beasts of the field and all the birds of the air. He brought them to the man to see what he would name them; and whatever the man called each living creature, that was its name.

Genesis 2:19

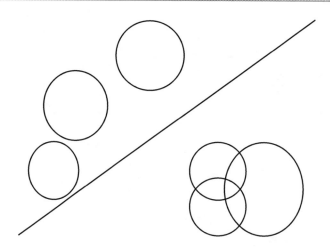

Which model is closer to nature: separate and easily differentiated species or overlapping types of body forms in an array which is difficult to classify?

CLASSIFICATION OF INANIMATE OBJECTS

Name:_____

Date:_____

Group: *Example*_____

Description: *One appendage sticking out of one side*

Elements:___*A I K*___ **No.** *3* = *23* %

Group: _____

Description: _____

Elements:_____ **No.**___ = ____%

Group: _____

Description: _____

Elements:_____ **No.**___ = ____%

Group: _____

Description: _____

Elements:_____ **No.**___ = ____%

Group: _____

Description: _____

Elements:_____ **No.**___ = ____%

Group: _____

Description: Rectangular

Elements:_____ **No.**___ = ____%

Group: _____

Description: Ovoid

Elements:_____ **No.**___ = ____%

Group: _____

Description: Square

Elements:_____ **No.**___ = ____%

Group: _____

Description: Round

Elements:_____ **No.**___ = ____%

Group: _____

Description: _____

Elements:_____ **No.**___ = ____%

Group: _____

Description: _____

Elements:_____ **No.**___ = ____%

Group: _____

Description: _____

Elements:_____ **No.**___ = ____%

Group: _____

Description: _____

Elements:_____ **No.**___ = ____%

CLASSIFICATION OF
INANIMATE OBJECTS

Name:_____
Date:_____

CRITICAL THINKING:

1. In the first step, in how many different sets were you able to group the drawings?

_____

_____

2. Were there any ambiguous drawings which were difficult to place? What was the reason for this difficulty?

_____

_____

_____

_____

_____

_____

_____

3. Did you have similar problems with the other steps? What about the classification system which you invented?

_____

_____

_____

_____

_____

_____

_____

_____

_____

4. When there were two or more sets into which a drawing could fit, how did you choose which set? Did you use random choice, or even numbers in each set? How do you justify your choice?

_____

_____

_____

_____

_____

_____

_____

_____

17 | Classification of Animals II

Here is a list of a few animals. Classify them according to the listed anatomical features. Use the chart to record your classification system. If you do not know the anatomical part of a specific organism, look it up.

Answer the questions after you are satisfied with your classification system.

Procedure I:

1. Make the first classification according to the support structure used by the animals.

2. Make the next classification according to body covering.

3. The third classification should be according to the reproductive system used by the animals.

4. The last classification should be according to habitat and food consumed.

> **Irish setter**
> **Sea cucumber**
> **Sponge**
> **Felis domesticus**
> **Pigeon**
> **Archeopteryx**
> **Rattle snake**
> **Shark**
> **Squirrel**
> **Dodo**
> **Sea turtle**
> **Mosquito**
> **Amoeba**
> **Coral**
> **Platypus**
> **Earthworm**
> **Snail**
> **Clam**
> **Bat**
> **Porpoise**
> **Crocodile**
> **Chicken**
> **Rana pipiens**
> **Ground hog**
> **Rabbit**
> **Dragonfly**
> **Euglena**
> **Shrimp**
> **Flounder**
> **Squirrel**
> **Crayfish**
> **Opossum**
> **Armadillo**

Procedure II:

Using the names of these biological groups, classify according to the same characteristics as the first chart.

> **Mammalia**
> **Vertebrata**
> **Echinodermata**
> **Mollusca**
> **Amphibia**
> **Aves**
> **Osteichthyes**
> **Reptilia**
> **Chondrichthyes**
> **Annelida**
> **Protista**

LAB 17: CLASSIFICATION OF ANIMALS II

	External Hard Skeleton	External Soft Skeleton	External Membrane	Soft, Cartilaginous Internal	Unarticulated Internal Hard	Articulated Internal Hard	Other Type
Support Systems							

	Scales	Feathers	Hair, Fur	Rough Skin	Smooth Skin, Hairless	Shell	Membrane
External Covering							

	Hard Shelled Egg	Soft, Jelly-like Eggs	Division	Live Birth, Placenta	Live Birth, Not Placenta	Soft, Leathery Eggs	Other Type
Method of Reproduction							

	Type Consumer	Marine: Pelagic (free swimming)	Marine: Benthic	Aquatic	Grassland	Desert	Forest
Carnivore							
Herbivore							

CLASSIFICATION OF ANIMALS II

Name:_____

Date:_____

Critical Thinking I:

1. Do some of the animals fit into more than one group? Do some of the animals seem to be borderline?

_____

_____

2. Do any of the groups seem to be made up of very dissimilar organisms?

_____

_____

3. In these cases, do you think that the classification systems have not worked? Why or why not?

_____

_____

4. If these animals do not always fit into neat, orderly classifications, what is the point of constructing such a system?

_____

_____

5. The platypus seems to be classified a mammal almost entirely on the basis of hair and milk. Do you agree with this classification? Explain.

_____

_____

Critical Thinking II:

1. Look up the terms Arthropoda, Echinodermata, Chordata, Amphibia. Do the terms seem to have meaning in regards to the animals they identify?

_____

_____

2. Why do you think that Latin was adopted as the language to use in the classification of organisms?

_____

_____

3. If a classification framework is developed around structure of the organisms, can you conclude that the organisms are related to each other? What other possible reasons could there be for similarity of form?

_____

_____

_____

_____

Nervous System:
18 | Reaction Time

MATERIALS
Ruler
Stopwatch
Notebook

The human nervous system is a complex design network constructed to receive sensation, communicate it, process the information, and react to it. However, one of the most remarkable abilities of the human nervous system is that it does much more than the function just described.

The thought which is described as 'independent' also begins within the brain and provokes action which may be independent of the environment. There is disagreement on the true independence of thought from the outside environment, but there are few who maintain that everything a human does or thinks is caused directly by the environment. The capacity for creativity in the human is unmeasured and is unique in quality, if not in presence among Earth dwellers.

This experiment does not involve creativity, though, except in what you plan to do with the results. The time necessary to react to an outside stimulus is a variable dependent upon many possible factors. A few of these might be fatigue, hunger, anxiety, panic, optimism, etc.

In the experiment you will attempt to trap a ruler as it descends between your open hands. A partner will drop the ruler. You will record the distance the ruler drops by using the scale on the ruler itself.

Once you have tried this a few times and gotten an average distance you have allowed the ruler to drop before catching it, you will attempt to change a few variables. This should give you a better idea of the factors which enhance or inhibit the rapid functioning of your nervous system.

In this experiment, the nervous system must sense the change in the ruler's status, relay the information to your brain, decide to close your hands, send the signal for hand closure to your arm muscles, cause your muscles to act, realize the pressure of ruler between the hands, and stop the action of the muscles. This sounds very complicated, and it is, but there are even more parts to the process I have left out. You should be surprised that the response can be as rapid as it is.

PROCEDURE:

1. Sit or stand with your hands 12 inches apart. Have your partner hold the top of a meter stick so that the zero mark is at the bottom and is between your hands.

2. Suddenly, your partner should drop the meter stick. You will try to catch the stick by trapping it between your hands. The release of the stick must be a surprise.

3. Record the measurement at the bottom of your hands. This is the distance which the meter stick fell before you trapped it. Repeat the action 10 times.

4. Now change a factor which might influence your reaction time. Record which variable you will be changing and make the trials again. Examples: loud sounds, just ate a candy bar, people yelling at you. See question 1.

5. Use at least three different variables. Before you actually perform the experiment, write your hypothesis down. Later, after you are done with the experiment, you must go back to your hypothesis and see if your data verify it. Remember, the word 'verify' comes from the Latin word for truth. In this experiment, you are attempting to determine truth. You will try to prove or disprove the truth of your hypothesis.

6. The charts you should draw for this experiment may be bar, line, or pie graphs. One bar or point for each average distance. Line charts are better for older students.

7. Why did your reaction times change, if they did? How could this information affect your performance in sports?

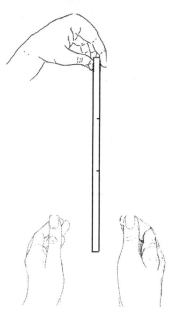

NERVOUS SYSTEM: REACTION TIME

Name:_____

Date:_____

Reaction time

Step 6: variable changes

Experiment 1: Control

Experiment 2: _____

Experiment 3: _____

Experiment 4: _____

Experiment 5: _____

Experiment 6: _____

Experiment 7: _____

Experiment 8: _____

Experiment 9: _____

Experiment 10: _____

Critical Thinking:

1. There are several types of fatigue which affect humans. Some of these are: lack of sleep, presence of too many people (as after shopping all morning), mental fatigue (like that after taking a three hour test), low blood sugar, eye fatigue or a recent large meal. Any or all of these can be measured. What do you hypothesize about the ways fatigue will affect you?

_____

_____

_____

Can you envision factors which might change your response to fatigue?

_____

If so, what might they be?

_____

_____

_____

2. Some of the types of fatigue listed above are more normally called stressors. In what way does stress relate to fatigue?

_____

_____

Are there possible multiple connections between stress and fatigue?

_____

_____

_____

_____

3. Look up this relationship at the library or perhaps you can discuss this with a doctor or some other person who would have access to some research on this area. Write an essay relating your findings in this experiment to the research you have done outside your laboratory. A suggested topic is: A factor which affects my reaction time and which might have other more far reaching effects on my health (or reaction speed, or fatigue level, or enjoyment of a sport, or success at video games, etc). There are many possible topics. Your topic must relate the experiment, you, and possible effects of your findings. Please include your sources in the reference list.

Trial Number	Experiment						
	1	2	3	4	5	6	7
1							
2							
3							
4							
5							
6							
7							
8							
9							
10							

Reaction Time

Experiment 1							
Experiment 2							
Experiment 3							
Experiment 4							
Experiment 5							
Experiment 6							
Experiment 7							
Experiment 8							
Experiment 9							
Experiment 10							

19 | Muscular System: Fatigue

MATERIALS
Watch with second hand
Graph paper
Three pound weight

A muscle is designed to perform basically one thing and that is the movement of some part of the body. The method which a muscle uses to propel the body part is contraction. By controlling the contraction and relaxation of various muscles or muscle groups the body can change its location. Functions within the body which require motion are dependent on the actions of muscles, that is, upon their contractions and relaxations.

The control of muscular contraction and relaxation is through the wiring diagram of the body: the nervous system. There are basically two types of control: one is automatic and requires no willful action command to take place, and the second is voluntary, the willful control of muscular contraction. Your text details more of this, so look there for more information.

In this experiment, you will make use of several muscles of the voluntary group. You have probably experienced muscle fatigue before, but today you will measure it.

Muscles need three things to contract and keep contracting efficiently: the command, the fuel, and the elimination of waste products.

First, the muscle needs the impulse, or the command to contract. This is a chemical command and so can be shorted out, stopped, or artificially induced much like a telephone call. There are some diseases that interfere with the nerves which carry the command messages. Some drugs can also block the progression of commands. There are certain injuries which block off messages. Some of the most interesting breakthroughs in medicine today are in this area of propagation of command impulses.

The fuel to perform work is also necessary to the muscle. Work is defined as the use of force which causes a change in location, or as we will say with muscles, a contraction. This contraction like any work requires fuel to be accomplished. The fuels of the body are: food, oxygen, and water.

The burning of fuel within the muscle cell creates waste products which are usually transported away from the muscle by the blood stream. When these wastes are allowed to build up, the muscle loses its ability to contract. Lactic acid build-up causes cramping, or the involuntary contraction

of the muscle cells. The muscle becomes tired. In marathons, runners must deal with this build up as their circulatory systems cannot carry away the waste products fast enough.

PROCEDURE:

1. If you are right handed, use your left hand for this experiment and visa versa if you are left handed.

2. Place the elbow of the arm you will use on the table while holding the weight down upon the table in the same hand.

3. Lift the weight until your lower arm is perpendicular to the table, lower the weight and repeat. This is the motion you will be performing for the experiment.

4. You will probably need a partner for this experiment. The partner will record the number of repetitions of the action you will be able to do in 20 second increments.

5. Have the partner record these numbers as you work.

6. Begin the motion and continue until the muscles are fatigued. If you continue past this point, your muscles will eventually not be able to contract any further until they are rested. If you exercise this far, you will become sore and the soreness will last several days until the muscles recover from their workout. This is not recommended, but will not damage the muscle. Be careful to do the repetitions without twisting the arm.

7. Take a break for one minute and then repeat this performance. Rest again and repeat a third time.

8. Plot your results on a chart with the horizontal axis labeled time in seconds and the vertical axis labeled in muscle contractions.

Note: For the students who are in great shape, use a set of muscles you rarely use. An example of this type is your little finger. You can attach a rubber band to the table, loop it around your little finger, and with the resistance of the rubber band, flex your finger. Even your index finger might get tired sooner than your biceps.

Student's arm showing motion of biceps to pull up the weight.

Note: Do not exercise to the point of extreme muscle fatigue as you will be sore.

MUSCULAR SYSTEM: FATIGUE

Name:_____

Date:_____

Critical Thinking:

1. In what ways do your three trials differ from each other?

_____

_____

_____

How do you explain this difference?

_____

_____

_____

_____

2. Did you find any evidence of muscular fatigue in this experiment?

_____

_____

Time Interval	Elapsed Time		Number of Muscle Contractions		
	Seconds	Minutes	Trial 1	Trial 2	Trial 3
20	20				
20	40				
20	00	1			
20					
20					
20					
20					
20					
20					
20					
20					
20					
20					
20					
20					
20					
20					
20					
20					

Using the ideas that muscles get energy from ATP and that they show fatigue when lactic acid builds up within the cells, explain your chart. Show when your muscles had lots of ATP and plenty of lactic acid.

_____

_____

3. Explain how the words "I am tired." could actually mean three different things dependent upon the three things necessary for muscle function. Suggest three solutions to the problem of fatigue in a certain muscle group.

_____

_____

4. Research the methods by which a marathon runner is able to keep going in spite of what you have learned about muscle fatigue. Write one page discussing this method including, if you can, any personal experiences on the topic.

_____

_____

_____

_____

Time Interval	Elapsed Time		Number of Muscle Contractions		
	Seconds	Minutes	Trial 4	Trial 5	Trial 6
20	20				
20	40				
20	00	1			
20					
20					
20					
20					
20					
20					
20					
20					
20					
20					
20					
20					
20					
20					
20					
20					
20					

MUSCULAR SYSTEM: FATIGUE

Number of muscle contractions ---->

20   40   60

Time (in seconds) ---->

20 | Population Succession Study

MATERIALS

Cover slips
Drawing paper
Dropper
Depression slides
Hay
Jar

Microscope
Petroleum jelly
Protozoan slowing agent
Rice
Water

When two types of organisms live together in the same local habitat, their relationship is important to the survival of both. The survival of the two is even more directly dependent upon the relationship between them when one of the species is the predator of the other.

As in chemistry, the limiting factor in a reaction sets the limits of the proceeding of the reaction. In ecology there is also a limiting factor. The abundance of the food supply regulates the growth of bacteria, plants, and higher life forms. The presence of too many of the organism will limit the rate of increase. The amount of space available and the oxygen supply also limit the growth of a population.

In this experiment, you will put together a predator-prey habitat. Within this environment, you will be able to count the prey and the predators and create charts which will show the relationship between the two.

Procedure:

1. Prepare a jar with distilled water in it. If the water has been chlorinated, place it on a shelf for a couple of days open to the air so that the chlorine gas may escape.

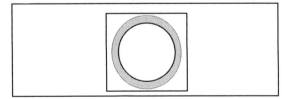

2. Obtain a small quantity of rice and hay or grass.

3. Place these in the non-chlorinated water of the jar and cover to several inches with the water. Stir and wait a day. Leave the lid off.

4. Prepare a depression slide with petroleum jelly. Put a thin line of petroleum jelly on the flat area around the depression (not in the depression). Place a few drops of water from the bottom of

the jar next to the sludge and organic material. Add a drop of protozoan slowing agent and cover with a cover slip. The petroleum jelly will seal off the depression from the air so that the water will not evaporate too quickly.

5. Once in the morning and once in the evening, take a dropper of water from the material in the bottom of the jar and make the observations.

6. Make drawings of the species you see. Record the number of each. This will be easier if you use lower power after you have identified the organisms. Keep a record on your drawing paper of the numbers.

Note: *When using hay and rice infusions, you should get ample populations of paramecia and amoebae. The amoebae will prey upon the paramecia. So, what you should have is a predator-prey succession scenario.*

Report:

Your report should have these parts:

1. Title page.

2. Purpose and preparation.

3. List of organisms found.

4. Drawings of all organism types.

5. Chart showing daily populations of paramecia and amoebae.

6. Graph showing population curves of each on the same chart.

7. Conclusion.

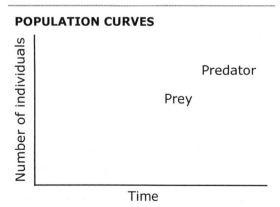

POPULATION CURVES

Lab Answers

Lab 2: Diffusion and Osmosis

1. Cup 1: should gain water weight

Cup 2: should stay the same

Cup 3: should lose water weight

2. Use your own data.

3. The bacteria will not grow. It may die or it may encyst.

4. If you were to reduce the antibacterial agent, the drying agent, in this case, the sugar, you run the risk of growing a good culture of bacteria.

5. The germinating seeds would lose water and the seedling would die. This happened in Carthage after the Romans sowed the fields with salt.

6. The weeds lose water on exposure to the salt and die. The salt does not disappear. Rains may take it on to places you may not wish to be salted. You could lose more than the weeds.

7. Water is removed from the fruit. You usually do this when making a fruit pie to make it juicy.

Lab 3: General Cell Structure in Animals

1. Different stains will color different parts of the cell, so by using different stains the biologist can see more clearly the parts of the organism. Try using some stains available like beet juice or berry juice. Ink might be useful.

2. The term organ refers to cells of a multicellular organism which are grouped together (usually) and perform a similar or related function. An organelle is a little organ. Within the single-celled organism, functions necessary for life (like digestion) must be performed just like in the multicellular organism. These specialized functions take place in the organelles. Organelles are not simple structures, but highly specialized features of the organism.

3. The question above deals with the topic of "simplicity". In the past, scientists have made assumptions about organisms, based upon the knowledge of the time. The information now available is that the structures of the single-celled organisms are not simple, but are very complex. They are very small but are very complex structures. You should have been able to observe at least some of these structures. The submicroscopic details of the organelles can not be seen with a microscope because they are so small. They can, however, be seen with an electron microscope which has the ability to capture very fine details.

4. The cells in a multicellular organism are specialized in form and function. They can not usually perform other activities and must even be fed by other cells specialized for that function. The one-celled organism, however, must perform all of the life functions within its own cytoplasmic membrane. By using this criterion of specialization and simplification of functions possible, the one-celled organism can be considered less simple.

5. Mitochondria would be expected to be numerous within a cell which must expend a great amount of energy. So, muscle cells could be expected to have the highest number of mitochondria. Cells require energy to perform functions like motion. This chemical energy must be transformed from food energy by the mitochondria. Without this process the energy would not be able to be used by the cell.

6. This is the place for your own hypothesis concerning the shape of a cell. Possible answers might include that the shape is determined by the method of feeding which the organism uses. In this way the proper food is easily caught or made. Another answer might be that the medium, or environment, determines the shape of the organism. These answers, while interesting ideas, would all result in the similarity of all the organisms of like feeding method, or of medium. These answers are still correct for this question even though they do not represent the whole picture.

7. The functions of reproduction and food getting are not performed by the red blood cells. These are controlled by the nucleus. If the functions are not needed, neither is the nucleus.

8. mitochondria - energy production

nucleus - reproduction, protein synthesis

vacuole - storage

cell membrane - protection / support

endoplasmic reticulum - support, protein synthesis, transport

ribosomes - protein synthesis

centrioles - reproduction

cytoplasm - support, transport

nucleolus - reproduction

golgi apparatus - storage, protein synthesis

Lab 4: Cellular Reproduction

1. The chromosomes are doubled so that there will be enough for each daughter cell to have a full set. 2x

2. See the answer above. Each chromosome is duplicated by acting as a template for itself.

3. RNA and DNA are made up of amino acids which are made from raw nutrients taken from the air. The nitrogen compounds are made from the nitrogen from the air and fertilizer; carbon compounds are made from the air. Without water these things still would be of little use to the plant for reproduction. Factors in the environment which would affect these things are the amount of rainfall, nitrogen in the soil, and light supply.

Lab 5: Protista: The Protozoans

Critical Thinking I

1. The amoeba causes a dangerous dysentery which is easier to prevent than to cure. Boiling water is the most common prevention but it does not destroy the encysted parasite. Treating the water with a poison like iodine tablets or chlorine is also used. Where the water is untreated, it should not be trusted.

2. The exchange of genetic material in the paramecium allows for the recombination of genes, some of which may be beneficial. If no recombination of genes is possible, some of the protists may not be able to survive environmental changes.

Critical Thinking II

1. A multinucleated organism may use the nuclei for redundant systems, that is, they would all be identical with the same type of job, or they might be specialized according to function.

2. A paramecium feeds on particles trapped in its gullet or oral groove. Its motion is a spin, as you could probably see, and so the organism covers a significant volume of space in its search for food. The cilia which line the oral groove help to trap the food particles in the gut.

3. The amoeba uses a different technique. The pseudopodia entrap the food, a paramecium perhaps, and engulf it. The pocket formed when this happens becomes a food vacuole and the digestion of the food takes place within it.

4. The amoeba is a predator, but you may have other predators in the mixed culture.

5. The amoeba can move by cytoplasmic streaming, by using pseudopodia as anchors to facilitate motion, and by flagella, if present.

Lab 6: Cell Structure: Plant

1. This is a thinking question. It should be clear that strong cell walls would increase the strength of the plant stem.

2. The chloroplasts of the corn plant are around the outer edge inside of the epidermis.

3. There is no cuticle over the stomata on the leaf as that would keep the gases from the spongy layer. This cuticle layer helps conserve the water in the leaf because it serves to keep water vapor from leaving the plant.

Lab 7: Internal Leaf Structure

1. $6 H_2O + 6 CO_2 ———> C_6H_{12}O_6 + 6 O_2$ in the presence of light.

2. The nutrients of the leaf (like in spinach) are within the cell membranes of the cells in the cytoplasm. The cell membrane, as well as the cytoplasm, is within the cell wall which needs to be ground to be broken.

3. An herbivore must have grinding teeth which can grind the cell walls. These teeth must have broad, flat surfaces.

4. Light reaction:

$$H_2O + 2ADP + 2P + 4 \text{ photons} ———> 2 ATP + 1/2 O_2$$

Dark reaction:

$$6 CO_2 + 18 ATP ———> C_6H_{12}O_6 + 18 ADP + 18 P + 6 H_2O$$ where ATP is adenosine triphosphate and ADP is adenosine diphosphate.

5. Oxygen is produced during the day in the light reaction. During the night, the gas produced is carbon dioxide.

6. Water is released by the leaves through the process of transpiration. This tends to make the atmosphere around the plants very humid. This is good for plant life. If the trees are cut down, the humidity of the environment is changed to make it less habitable for plants.

7. The spongy layer is the middle layer of the leaf. This layer has holes in it which hold the gases necessary to the process of photosynthesis.

8. Pesticides can be absorbed by the leaf through the stomata if the cuticle protected the rest of the leaf. Also, the underside of the leaf may not be covered by the cuticle.

9. Sprayed-on fertilizer is used effectively to fertilize plants.

Lab 8: Plant Anatomy: Stems

1. The phloem cells conduct the food produced by the plant and stored in other locations, like the root in the potato. The xylem conducts the water from the ground as well as the minerals dissolved in it.

2. In the tree the water is conducted up the stem by the xylem which is closer to the center of the tree than is the phloem. The phloem is separated from the xylem by the cambium. In the herbaceous dicot, the arrangement is very similar, but these tissues are located in a ring of vascular bundles around the edge of the stem.

3. The epidermis goes around the outside of the stem in all plants. This is the 'skin' of the plants. It serves to protect the plant and keep the nutrients, like water and minerals, flowing in the plant instead of leaking out.

4. The phloem is on the outside of the vascular bundles. This tissue carries the food produced in the photosynthesis parts of the plant. This sounds like what an aphid would like for dinner.

Lab 9: Plant Anatomy: Roots

1. Ideally, the root ball should be the same size as the leafy top. In practice, this is not practical for large trees, as the root ball would be too large. The amount of root surface area should be about equal to the amount of leaf area.

2. The roots do not move themselves. Hydrotropism refers to the tendency of a root to grow more on the side nearest to the water supply.

3. The position under the leafy canopy is not a good place for smaller plants. The water for the smaller plant is taken by the larger tree. As well, the light for the smaller plant is taken so that the smaller plant is in the shade. Photosynthesis requires light. Because of these reasons, the smaller plant will be stunted. The exception to this are those plants which thrive in these conditions. An example of this is the orchid which grows in tropical trees, living on decayed matter in recesses in the trees and on water trapped there.

4. Xylem transports the water up from the ground through non-living cell walls called tracheids and vessels. They have holes through the cell walls for the passage of water. The fibers of the xylem strengthen the stem.

Phloem through the sieve-tube members conduct materials through the stem and the leaves.

Root hairs are single-celled extensions of epidermal cells on the root which absorb water and minerals from the soil.

5. The secondary roots begin in the pericycle and as they grow, push out through the layers of the root.

6. Carrot- whole root

   Radish- whole root

   Potato- this is really a stem

   Turnips- whole root

Lab 10: Reproduction: Pollen Germination

1. It happens that insects are attracted to yellow. This should help out when it is time to pollinate the flowers.

2. Some plants are pollinated by the wind, others by insects, and still others just fall onto the stigma. The different techniques require different shapes and textures for optimum chance at fertilization.

3. Write your own hypothesis, then prove it using your own data.

4. The pollen season lasts from spring through fall which is a long time to be subjected to pollen if you are allergic. It is good that most types of pollen are only around for a few weeks.

Lab 11: Clam Dissection

1. The muscle must be connected to the shell itself in order to get the leverage necessary to close the shell tightly. No other part of the clam would produce as much strength and support for a muscle. Since the mantle does not cover the part of the shell to which the muscle is attached, the inner layer of pearl would not be deposited by the mantle there.

2. Pearls are formed when the bivalve covers a grain of sand or other intrusion with a pearly layer similar to the inner part of the shell. This layer helps the clam avoid the irritation of the intrusion. Pearls may be round, but not always. They are sometimes even attached to the shell.

3. Use your own data.

4. An indicator of pollution should respond to a decrease in the quality of the environment quickly and at small changes. This will enable scientists to measure small changes before they become large changes to an environment. The clam is a filter feeder and is therefore dependent upon what floats in the water, both for breath and for food. A reason that the clam enjoys clean water is that dirty water usually has a low dissolved oxygen content on which the clam depends for gas exchange.

5. The foot-intestine combination is good for saving space within the small volume of the shell. Also, the body of the foot is little used in the clam and a good spot for another organ. Another dual function in the clam are the gill cilia which propel the food particles towards the mouth at the same time that they move the water containing the dissolved oxygen for the clam to breathe past the absorbing structures of the gills.

6. One might assume that the clam lived in shallow, clear water which had a good supply of nutrients moving past the clam. Clams enjoy certain specific temperatures of the water and this fossil one probably also had a specific temperature in which it lived. The bottom was probably sandy or rocky, not muddy. The clam needs clear waters, not water which has suspended sediment which will obstruct the gas exchanges.

Lab 12: Earthworm Dissection

1. If the earthworm did not have a closed circulatory system, the blood would tend to pool in the rear of the earthworm's body. This is because of the repetitive constrictions of the muscles during the motion of the worm.

2. Red.

3. The setae hold the earthworm in position so that the worm can propel itself forward instead of remaining in place.

4. The longitudinal muscles of the earthworm contract and relax in sequence. The setae hold the worm in place while the worm moves forward. The muscles are lengthwise on the worm as is their contraction.

5. The anus is at the end of the worm allowing the disposal of undigested food in a place which will not interfere with the ingestion of fresh food. It also allows the worm to use the longitudinal motion of its muscles to propel food through the digestive system and out of the anus without stopping its motion. Disposal would restrict the movements of the worm or it would prevent all of the undigested food from leaving the body at once.

6. Segmentation can be an advantage when the worm is damaged in some area which is duplicated in another segment. It would tend to isolate damage to the worm.

Lab 13: Grasshopper Dissection

1. The support function of the grasshopper is met by the exoskeleton. There is no internal skeleton.

2. There are small ligaments and muscles attached to the inside of the leg joints which will propel the organism.

3. The mouth parts of the grasshopper cut its food by sliding and slicing across each other. The palps help the organism support its food while it is being cut up.

4. The last leg which is attached to the metathorax appears to be designed for jumping. You can observe that it is bent and only needs to be extended for a jump.

Lab 14: Fish Dissection

1. Use your own data for the age of the fish. The layers of the scale are laid down by the year, having thicker layers laid down during years of good food supplies.

2. The fish gets its oxygen through gas exchange within the gills. Carbon dioxide is given off. Have you noticed bubbles in an aquarium? Some will be oxygen given off by the algae and some will be carbon dioxide given off by the fish. The source of the oxygen is the water. Yes, there are similarities between gills and lungs. They both extract oxygen from the surrounding medium and give off carbon dioxide.

3. The spines serve as protectors for the fish against predation from larger fish. They deter swallowing by predators.

4. The teeth of the fish are not useful in chewing or grinding, but are good for holding on to prey which will be swallowed whole.

5. The fish can smell. You would not normally think of a sense of smell in the water, but water, through currents and Brownian motion, will carry molecules of things very far very quickly. These molecules can be detected by the sense of smell. You are doing the same thing when you smell perfume across the room from someone. You are detecting molecules of the perfume which have been transported through the air to your side of the room.

6. The air bladder enables the fish to change depths in the water at will. The amount of air within can be increased to rise and decreased to sink. The location of the air bladder is optimum for the fish in that it is close to the balance point (center of buoyancy) of the fish. This is much the same idea as you observe when you try to float on top of a kick board. It is easier the closer you get it to your balance point.

7. The gill rakers of the fish increase the surface area of the gill increasing the efficiency of gas absorption. They also provide support for the gills themselves, keeping them separated to expand the volume of water they are breathing in. The opercula, or gill covers, keep the water flow smooth across the fish increasing its streamlining.

8. The fins face to the posterior as a protective device, but they also have reduced drag in the position. The front view of a fish is very small and that is the area of most drag for the fish. Having a small exposed area reduces this drag.

Lab 15: Fetal Pig Dissection

1. To the lungs where the blood will become oxygenated and be sent back to the heart for distribution to the rest of the body.

2. The kidney dialysis machine purifies the blood of the toxic wastes which would continue to build up in the blood stream if not removed. The poisons will eventually build up in the tissues of the ill person. These functions would have been done by the kidneys. The schedule of purification by the dialysis machine is dependent upon the degree of damage to the natural kidneys of the patient.

3. The unborn child has no way to plan for its birth, but its designer did. The birth process will be a time during which the baby's oxygen supply may not be consistent. If the baby has an oversupply of red blood cells there should be plenty of oxygen in the system to last for the duration of birth.

4. The human like the pig has this separation. The speed of a reaction is increased if the reaction can take place without thinking consciously about it. We call this an automatic reaction.

Lab 16: Classification of Animals I

The questions which accompany this experience should be dependent upon your own systems of classification. If you have chosen groups based upon the types of appendages, number B would fit into several groups: 1. solid appendages, 2. lightly dashed appendages, and 3. darkly dashed appendages.

Troublesome classifications will most likely be B, E, F, L, M, J, and C. Others may be double classified depending upon your system. Suggested systems are: color shading, shape, source, type of corner, number of appendages.

Lab 17: Classification of Animals II

Critical Thinking I

You will discover that the feature of the animal which you use to classify your group determines the group. Many different characteristics are repeated from group to group. An example is the use of a hard exoskeleton. Many widely separated organisms use this form of support and protective structure. Examples are the echinoderm, the arthropods, the turtle (which also uses an internal skeleton for support, but the shell for protection), coral, snail, and even the armadillo (which has an internal skeleton, but uses a hard, tough armor derived from hair on the outside for protection, not for support.).

Critical Thinking II

1. Arthropoda- jointed legs. Echinoderms- spiny skinned. Chordata- nerve chord or backbone. Amphibia- two lives, or two habitats.

2. Latin was a good choice for the classification system because of the number of languages around the world. The word for dog is different in every place, or it may be similar but not quite the same. This could (and does) lead to confusion when discussing an animal (or plant). By using Latin these problems are avoided.

3. No, because there are many dissimilar organisms which have common structures. For example, insects, bats, and birds all have similarity of form in that they all have wings. However, they are not related at all. It is very likely that organisms which are not similar at all share structures that have a common form and function because God created them that way. For example, He knew which organisms needed to fly and so created them with wings. The same is true for all structures that have similar function and form but are found on completely unrelated organisms.

Lab 18: Nervous System: Reaction Time

These questions all ask for your own thoughts on this topic. A stressor causes the body to produce adrenalin which heightens the reactions. This action causes the metabolism to speed up. In this way, a stressor causes fatigue.

Hopefully, this experiment will cause the student to become more aware of his/her own body's reaction to stress and fatigue.

Lab 19: Muscular System & Fatigue

1. The student should explain the differences between the trials by differences in the amount of chemical energy available, the fatigue level, and/or the amount of lactic acid build-up in the muscle.

2. ATP represents the potential energy of the muscle, so when there is a lot of ATP, the muscle should be most energetic. Lactic acid should result in cramps and fatigue in the muscle, so lots of lactic acid should be present when the muscles are tired and cannot do as many repetitions.

3. At least three different things can be meant by the phrase: "I am tired." 1. The body is out of fuel, so the muscles have no source of chemical energy. 2. The muscles have a build-up of lactic acid or some other waste product in them, producing cramps or the inability to continue to contract. 3. The brain may be signalling to the body to stop doing this boring activity, hence, I am tired.

4. Your own data.

LAB 17: CLASSIFICATION OF ANIMALS II

Support Systems

External Hard Skeleton	External Soft Skeleton	External Membrane	Soft, Cartilaginous Internal	Unarticulated Internal Hard	Articulated Internal Hard	Other Type
clam coral snail	dragonfly shrimp crayfish mosquito	euglena amoeba earthworm sea cucumber Protista	shark	sponge	pigeon Archeopteryx rattle snake dodo sea turtle platypus bat porpoise crocodile Mammalia Vertebrata Amphibia Aves Osteichthyes Reptilia chicken Rana pipiens ground hog rabbit flounder squirrel oppossum armadillo Irish setter Felis domesticus	other type

External Covering

Scales	Feathers	Hair, Fur	Rough Skin	Smooth Skin, Hairless	Shell	Membrane
Osteichthyes flounder	Aves chicken pigeon dodo Archeopteryx	Mammalia (many in list)	Chondrichthyes Reptilia Echinodermata shark rattle snake crocodile	Protista Annelida earthworm amoeba euglena	Mollusca clam snail	Protista amoeba euglena

Method of Reproduction

Hard Shelled Egg	Soft, Jelly-like Eggs	Division	Live Birth, Placenta	Live Birth, Not Placenta	Soft, Leathery Eggs	Other Type
chicken	Amphibia Osteichthyes Rana pipens flounder	Protista amoeba	Mammalia (many in list)	Chondrichthyes shark	Reptilia snake rattle snake platypus (mammal)	other type

Type Consumer

Type Consumer	Marine: Pelagic (free swimming)	Marine: Benthic	Aquatic	Grassland	Desert	Forest
Carnivore	shark flounder shrimp porpoise	coral sea cucumber sponge clam	mosquito (larvae) amoeba crayfish	Irish setter Felis domesticus armadillo	rattle snake armadillo	dragonfly opossum bat
Herbivore	sea turtle		euglena (also producer)	pigeon ground hog rabbit chicken		squirrel